SIZE AND SHAPE CHANGES OF CONTRACTILE POLYMERS

Conversion of Chemical into Mechanical Energy

eminar on Polymer Science, University College, London, 1957.

Size and Shape Changes of Contractile Polymers

CONVERSION OF CHEMICAL INTO MECHANICAL ENERGY

PROCEEDINGS OF SEMINARS HELD AT UNIVERSITY COLLEGE, LONDON

Edited by

A. WASSERMANN

SYMPOSIUM PUBLICATIONS DIVISION

PERGAMON PRESS

NEW YORK · OXFORD · LONDON · PARIS

1960

PERGAMON PRESS INC.
122 *East* 55th *Street, New York* 22, *N.Y.*
P.O. Box 47715, *Los Angeles, California*

PERGAMON PRESS LTD.
Headington Hill Hall, Oxford
4 & 5 *Fitzroy Square, London, W*.1

PERGAMON PRESS S.A.R.L.
24 *Rue des Écoles, Paris V*ᵉ

PERGAMON PRESS G.m.b.H.
Kaiserstrasse 75, *Frankfurt am Main*

Library of Congress Card No. 60–14950

PRINTED IN GREAT BRITAIN BY ADLARD & SON LTD., DORKING

CONTENTS

INTRODUCTION

CONTINUING earlier Seminars[1]* on Polymer Science in the Chemistry Department of University College, London, lectures on size and shape changes of contractile systems and conversion of chemical into mechanical energy were given in July 1957 and April 1958. Miss S. Stratford-Lawrence, Editor at Pergamon Press Ltd., suggested that the Proceedings of these two Seminars should be published and that I should help in the task. Without criticizing the various contributions, taken separately, some people will argue that it is not a good scheme to publish them together, because the whole field has not been covered: strain-stress relationships of rubber-like materials,[2] transitions from crystalline to amorphous polymers,[3] shape of muscle proteins as determined by electron microscopy[4] or light scattering[5] methods and theories of muscular activity[6] are all related topics which are not discussed in this monograph. Furthermore the time between the date of the Seminars and that of publication is long and the presentation of the papers is unequal, there being a short review article and detailed descriptions of unpublished research. While all these shortcomings are admitted, this monograph makes it clear, nevertheless, that a fundamental advance has been made, during the last years, in our knowledge of conversion of chemical into mechanical energy by means of contractile polymers and of the structure of biologically important fibres by means of X-ray diffraction investigations. It is shown, furthermore, that a distinction must be made between chemically and energy linked processes in applying the high energy phosphate bond concept, and that the stoicheiometry and mechanism of mechanochemical processes, including those leading to isothermal melting of partially crystalline polymers, are not sufficiently studied. Publications, stimulating research in these fields are useful. I believe that this monograph will have a favourable influence in this direction.

A. W.

Chemistry Department, University
College, London, W.C.1.

* For references see overleaf.

REFERENCES

1. *Nature* **171**, 65 (1953); **172**, 102 (1954); **175**, 670 (1955); **178**, 18 (1956); **180**, 535 (1957).
2. L. R. C. TRELOAR, *The Physics of Rubber Elasticity*, Oxford University Press, 1949.
3. P. J. FLORY, *Science* **124**, 53 (1956); *J. Am. Chem. Soc.* **78**, 5222 (1956); *J. Cell. Comp. Physiol.* **49**, Suppl. 1, **175** (1957); L. MANDELKENN, D. E. ROBERTS, A. F. DIORIO, and A. S. POSNER, *J. Am. Chem. Soc.* **81**, 4148 (1959); there are also references to pertinent earlier literature. Cf. also J. B. SPEAKMAN, *J. Text. Inst.* (Mather Lecture) **32**, 183 (1944); *J. Roy. Soc. Arts* **93**, 603 (1945); J. L. MONGAR and A. WASSERMANN, *Nature* **159**, 746 (1947); J. L. MONGAR and A. WASSERMANN, *J. Chem. Soc.* 500 (1952) and footnotes 7 and 8 on page 107 of this volume (article by COOPER and WASSERMANN).
4. H. E. HUXLEY, *Proc. Roy. Soc.* B **141**, 59 (1953); *Biochem. Biophys. Acta* **12**, 387 (1953); J. HANSON and H. E. HUXLEY, *Symp. Soc. Exptl. Biol.* **9**, 228 (1955); *Biochem. Biophys. Acta* **23**, 229, 250 (1957); H. E. HUXLEY, *J. Biophys. Biochem. Cytol.* **3**, 631 (1957).
5. P. GEIDUSCHEK and A. HOLZER, *Advances in Biological and Medical Physics* **6**, 431 (1958).
6. D. R. WILKIE, *Progress in Biophysics* **4**, 288 (1954).

1

ELEMENTARY MECHANOCHEMICAL PROCESSES

by A. Katchalsky, S. Lifson, I. Michaeli and
M. Zwick

The Weizmann Institute of Science, Rehovoth, Israel

1. INTRODUCTION

1.1. Natural contractile systems have attracted continued interest of physiologists, biochemists and biophysicists for many decades. Recent advances in the isolation of contractile elements from the muscle[1] have increased the scientific activity in the field and it is now felt that an understanding of biological mechanochemistry is an achievable goal. Further stimulus has been obtained from the study of synthetic fibres which are able to transform chemical into mechanical energy in isothermal cycles.[2] Some promising models have been proposed on which the fundamental notions of the theory of mechanochemistry could be worked out and clarified.[3]

It is realized however that a treatment of the natural contraction process, say the twitch of the muscle, is an irreversible process.[4] In order to advance towards an exact formal description of the complicated relaxation phenomena involved in the contraction a preliminary treatment, that of the elementary equilibrium properties and reversible processes in the contractile systems, has to be carried out.

The theoretical analysis of the reversible mechanochemical systems presented in this paper is not concerned with the particular behaviour of either natural or synthetic contractile fibres. It is devoted to the formulation of the necessary conditions for mechano-chemical performance and to the adaptation of classical thermo-dynamic concepts and equations to the study of mechanochemical systems.

1.2. We use the term "mechanochemical system" to designate thermodynamic systems capable of transforming chemical energy directly into mechanical work or conversely of transforming mechanical into chemical potential energy. These transformations are carried out in an "engine" capable of performing cyclically, reverting after each cycle to its initial state. With the completion of a cycle all changes are found in the external world surrounding the engine, the changes being a transfer of reactive substances from one chemical potential to another, with a corresponding performance of mechanical work. In some work cycles, such as that of the muscle, the reactant falls from a high chemical potential to a lower one and the engine liberates mechanical energy; however, opposite cycles may be envisaged in which the application of mechanical energy may raise the chemical potential of a substance and permit its transfer from a reservoir of a lower chemical potential to a reservoir of a higher potential.

Much attention has been paid recently to the chemical changes introduced by mechanical working of plastic materials. Such processes are sometimes called "mechanochemical". They are, however, not included in our considerations since these processes are not suitable for cyclical mechanochemical performance typical for mechanochemical engines.

We shall consider in the following the "engine" to be a fibre or bundle of fibres made of reactive macromolecules. Although engines made of non-polymeric materials may be envisaged, it is only certain polymeric materials which play a prominent role both in nature and in man-made mechanochemical systems; these materials have a ready coupling of chemical reaction with chemical performance and are able both to sustain appreciable mechanical stresses and undergo appreciable dimensional changes on absorbing reactive substances. However, the following treatment is not dependent on either the chemical nature of the fibres or on the type of the reaction which the fibre-engine undergoes.

An engine should be able to maintain contact with reservoirs containing reactants at different levels of chemical potential. In order to maintain the potential difference and to prevent the reactant from spontaneous irreversible reaction the reservoirs have to be provided with suitable isolating mechanisms. That is to say, the engine has to be able to make contact with, or to get isolated from, the reservoirs. The isolating mechanism is not only the rigid wall of a container but may be any of the numerous isolating mechanisms of biological systems and in a more general sense it may even be a potential barrier which prevents reaction to take place and which may be removed by a catalytic action.

It should be stressed that in certain phases of a mechano-chemical cycle the engine acts as an open thermodynamic system, while in other phases it must be closed towards some or all components of its environment. The distinction between processes in closed and open thermodynamic systems is essential in the mechanochemical analysis.

1.3. A simple mechanochemical process in an open system is the swelling of gels under stress. The fundamental relations connected with the absorption of liquids by any solids under stress have been given by Gibbs[5] and elucidated in the commentary of Rice.[6] Barkas specified the general equations of Gibbs to the absorption of water vapour on wood[7] and the equations were developed further by Warburton[8] and Gurney.[9] Numerous relations were advanced by Gee[10] and Treloar[11] in order to provide convenient expressions for the experimental verification of the theories of Flory-Rehner and of Kuhn for the behaviour of swollen polymeric networks under stress. The thermodynamics of infinitesimal deformation of swollen solids was carefully analysed and summarized by Hermans.[12] Hill[13] and White[14] considered the absorbtion under finite strain and developed expressions for the analysis of experimental data.

1.4. The work of authors cited above provides essential elements for the description of the separate steps of a mechanochemical process. Further study, however, had to be made in order to combine the available information into an integrated description of a cyclically operating engine. The study of mechanochemical cycles was introduced by Katchalsky[15] and by Kuhn and Hargitay.[16] Their analysis was concerned with cycles of polyelectrolyte gels, however they made use of several thermodynamic concepts of general validity. A further step was taken by Morales and Botts[17] and by Hill and Morales[18] who specified a number of requirements for a mechanochemical engine operating in cycles. Their treatment was based on definite models for muscular working substance and included both thermodynamic and kinetic requirements, but was not sufficiently general to represent the fundamental characteristics of any possible reversible mechanochemical system.

1.5. The present paper is devoted to a systematic development of the concepts and equations pertinent to the description of a general reversible mechanochemical system. In Section 2 we consider differential expressions for elementary steps and derive a set of useful cross relations between various differential coefficients. Section 3 is devoted to a general consideration of mechanochemical cycles and their geometrical representation. Section 4 is concerned with the analysis of elementary cycles and with the formulation of criteria for mechanochemical performance. In order to illustrate the use of the general results of Sections 2–4 we apply these results in Section 5 to the "autone" model, which was introduced by several authors[19, 20, 21] for the description of muscular contractility.

2. THERMODYNAMICS OF MECHANOCHEMICAL CHANGE

2.1. *Thermodynamic potentials*

2.1.1. In the present section we shall introduce the thermodynamic framework required for the treatment of mechanochemical systems. Let us consider the most general change in the internal energy dU of the engine. It is given by the fundamental equation of Gibbs:

$$dU = TdS - dW + \sum_i \mu_i dn_i + \psi d\epsilon + \ldots \tag{1}$$

where dS is the increase in the entropy of the engine at a temperature T, dW is the mechanical work performed by the engine, dn_i is the amount of the ith component introduced from the reservoir into the engine at a chemical potential μ_i, $\psi d\epsilon$ is the electrical work term due to a change in the charge $d\epsilon$ at an electrostatic potential ψ, etc. We shall assume that only thermal, mechanical and chemical terms participate in the process so that all the terms $\psi d\epsilon$, etc. will be omitted in the following.

The mechanical term dW was considered in detail by Gibbs and analysed recently by Hermans.[12] In the case of non-isotropic solids dW is expressed in terms of the stresses p_{jk} and the strains e_{jk}, well known from the theory of elasticity,

$$dW = V \sum_{jk=1}^{3} p_{jk} e_{jk},$$

where V denotes the volume of the solid. However, in the case of homogeneous gels, i.e. when the stresses are constant throughout the substance it is preferable, as shown by Hermans, to express the mechanical work in terms of the forces f_j and the infinitesimal displacements dl_j

$$dW = \sum_{j=1}^{3} f_j dl_j.$$

In the following we shall consider the engine to consist of elongated homogeneous fibres of length l, of uniform cross section along the fibre, stretched by a force f. For this fibre engine the work term reduces to $dW = pdV - fdl$ and the Gibbs equation assumes the form

$$dU = TdS - pdV + fdl + \sum_i \mu_i dn_i. \qquad (2)$$

Equation (2) leaves out of consideration those chemical components whose quantity does not change in the process. However, the integral form of the function U should include also the term corresponding to the number n_p of the molecules which constitute the mechanochemical fibre. The internal energy of the engine is therefore to be written as

$$U = TS - pV + fl + \sum_i \mu_i n_i + \mu_p n_p, \qquad (3)$$

where the function of state U is expressed as a sum of state functions.

The set of characteristic measurable properties on the right hand side of eq. (3) define unequivocally the state of a thermodynamic system. Thus the $2s + 8$ variables of state T, S, p, V, f, l, μ_i, n_i, μ_p and n_p fully describe the state of a mechanochemical system. However, not all of the variables are independent. In eq. (2) the independent variables of state are the extensive properties while the conjugate intensive variables are given by the corresponding partial derivatives of the internal energy. The number of independent variables is therefore half the total number of state variables, i.e. in our case $s + 4$, and at p, T and n_p constant it reduces to $s + 1$.

2.1.2. The choice of a given set of independent variables can be done in many ways. Of special interest are those sets where each variable is one out of a pair of conjugate variables. To each set there corresponds a function, which is called the *thermodynamic potential* of the set of variables. The thermodynamic potentials and their differentials are constructed in the following way:

Let us denote the intensive properties by P_ρ and their extensive conjugates by K_ρ. Thus P_ρ stands for T, p, f, μ_i and μ_p while K_ρ denotes the corresponding S, V, l, n_i and n_p. With this notation the internal energy will be written as

$$U = \sum_{\rho=1}^{s+4} P_\rho K_\rho, \tag{4}$$

where the summation is taken over all the $s + 4$ independent variables. Similarly, the Gibbs equation (eq. 2) assumes the form

$$dU = \sum_{\rho=1}^{s+4} P_\rho dK_\rho. \tag{5}$$

To build other thermodynamic potentials we pick out any number r of conjugate pairs and combine them with U according to eq. (6).

$$\Psi^{(r)} = U - \sum_{\rho=1}^{r} P_\rho K_\rho. \tag{6}$$

The number of such r-termed thermodynamic potentials is evidently

$$\binom{s+4}{r}$$

and the total number of all possible thermodynamic potentials with r ranging from zero to $i + 4$ is

$$\sum_{r=0}^{s+4} \binom{s+4}{r} = 2s + 4. $$

Introducing the Gibbs equation (eq. 5) we get for the total differential of $\psi^{(r)}$

$$d\Psi^{(r)} = dU - d\left(\sum_{\rho=1}^{r} P_\rho K_\rho\right) = \sum_{\rho=r+1}^{s+4} P_\sigma dK_\sigma - \sum_{\rho=1}^{r} K_\rho dP_\rho, \tag{7}$$

where ρ is the running index from 1 to r and σ the running index from $r + 1$ to $s + 4$. It may be noted that the potential $\Psi^{(s+4)}$ for $r = s + 4$ is identically zero

$$\Psi^{(s+4)} = U - \sum_{\rho=1}^{s+4} P_\rho K_\rho = 0. \tag{8}$$

Its corresponding differential expression

$$d\Psi^{(s+4)} = 0 = - \sum_{\rho=1}^{s+4} K_\rho dP_\rho, \tag{9}$$

will be readily recognized as the Gibbs–Duhem equation. All the independent variables of this potential are intensive.

For any choice of independent variables in eq. (7), the dependent variables are obtained from the corresponding potential $\Psi^{(r)}$. Let P_ρ be one of the independent intensive variables. The conjugate extensive dependent variable K_ρ is derived by the relation

$$\frac{\partial \Psi^{(r)}}{\partial P_\rho} = - K_\rho \qquad 1 \leqslant \rho \leqslant r. \tag{10}$$

The partial differentiation is carried out in such a manner that except P_ρ all other extensive or intensive independent variables are kept constant. Similarly, the conjugates of the extensive independent variables are given by the relations

$$\frac{\partial \Psi^{(r)}}{\partial K_\sigma} = P_\sigma \qquad r + 1 \leqslant \sigma \leqslant s + 4, \tag{11}$$

where again, except K_σ, all other extensive or intensive independent variables are kept constant. As a rule in each partial differentiation of a thermodynamic potential with respect to any one of its independent variables all the other independent variables are kept constant. We shall often make use of this rule in order to spare the cumbersome notation of all the variables which are kept constant.

The dependent variables P_σ and K_ρ as derived from $\Psi^{(r)}$ are functions of all the corresponding independent variables. The $s + 4$ relations $P_\sigma (K_\sigma, P_\rho)$ and $K_\rho (K_\sigma, P_\rho)$ are known as "equations of state" of the system. The explicit form of the equations of state has to be found experimentally or derived from a knowledge of molecular properties, by the methods of statistical mechanics.

2.2 *Differential capacities and cross coefficients of a mechanochemical interest*

2.2.1. In the following we shall find it useful to describe certain properties of mechanochemical systems by considering their "differential capacities". The differential capacities express the change of the extensive variable with the change of the conjugate intensive variable—thus $\partial l/\partial f$ is the mechanical differential capacity of the engine while $\partial n_i/\partial \mu_i$ is the chemical or "buffering" capacity of the ith component in the fibre. It will be observed that these capacities are defined in a manner similar to that of the electrical differential capacity $\partial \epsilon/\partial \psi$. More explicitly the mechanical capacity measures the change in length corresponding to a unit change in the stretching force, while the chemical capacities give the number of moles which have to be absorbed into the fibre to bring about a unit increase in the conjugate chemical potential.

The differential capacities $\partial P_\sigma/\partial K_\sigma$ are by eq. (11) second derivatives of the corresponding thermodynamic potentials

$$\frac{\partial P_\sigma}{\partial K_\sigma^2} = \frac{\partial^2 \Psi^{(r)}}{\partial K_\sigma}. \tag{12}$$

It is readily realized that the differential capacities may be obtained under different restrictions. Take for example $(\partial l/\partial f)_{\mu_i}$, the change of the length l with force f acting on a fibre when the fibre is open to a reservoir and maintains a constant chemical potential μ_i of the reactive substance in the fibre. It will in general be different from $(\partial l/\partial f)_{n_i}$ i.e. from the dependence of l on f in a closed system which prevents the entrance of n_i into the fibre. The different capacities are derived from different thermodynamic potentials. Since the thermodynamic potentials are interrelated through equations of the type of eq. (6) there must exist thermodynamic relations between $(\partial l/\partial f)_{n_i}$ and $(\partial l/\partial f)_{\mu_i}$; similarly a relation has to exist between $(\partial n_i/\partial \mu_i)_f$ and $(\partial n_i/\partial \mu_i)_l$ describing the changes in the number of moles of the absorbed reactant per unit change of the chemical potential at either constant force or constant length.

2.2.2. The structure of the thermodynamic potentials implies the existence of cross relations or, as they are sometimes called, Maxwell relation between any two pairs of non-conjugated terms. These cross relations play an important role in the evaluation of mechanochemical data. Thus, for example, the identity

$$\frac{\partial^2 \Psi^{(r)}}{\partial P_\rho \partial P_\rho'} = \frac{\partial^2 \Psi^{(r)}}{\partial P_\rho' \partial P_\rho}, \qquad l \leqslant \rho, \rho' \leqslant r, \tag{13}$$

leads to the following equality of the differential coefficients

$$\frac{\partial K_\rho}{\partial P_\rho'} = \frac{\partial K_\rho'}{\partial P_\rho}. \tag{14}$$

These differential coefficients will be denoted as cross- or coupling-coefficients. The variables held constant in eq. (14) are determined by the thermodynamic potential from which K_ρ and K'_ρ are derived. Similarly, we have

$$\frac{\partial P_\sigma}{\partial K_\sigma} = \frac{\partial P'_\sigma}{\partial K_\sigma} \qquad r+1 \leqslant \sigma,\ \sigma' \leqslant s+4, \tag{15}$$

and

$$\frac{\partial P_\sigma}{\partial P_\rho} = \frac{\partial K_\rho}{\partial K'_\sigma} \qquad 1 \leqslant \rho \leqslant r,\ r+1 \leqslant \sigma \leqslant s+4. \tag{16}$$

Thus for any potential we have

$$\binom{s+4}{2}$$

possible cross relations and the total number of possible cross relations is therefore

$$\binom{s+4}{2} \cdot 2^{s+4}.$$

This number is rather large, and even in the case of a fibre engine reacting with a bicomponent bath ($s = 2$) at constant p, T and n_p, we have

$$\binom{3}{2} 2^3 = 24.$$

The cross relations at constant p, T and n_p may be classified in four groups,

$$\frac{\partial n_i}{\partial \mu_j} = \frac{\partial n_j}{\partial \mu_i};\ \frac{\partial n_i}{\partial n_j} = -\frac{\partial \mu_j}{\partial \mu_i};\ \frac{\partial f}{\partial n_i} = \frac{\partial \mu_i}{\partial l};\ \frac{\partial f}{\partial \mu_i} = -\frac{\partial n_i}{\partial l},$$

where the independent variables kept constant in the partial differentiations are determined by the choice of the thermodynamic potential from which the cross relation is derived. For the sake of compactness and convenient reference we introduce the logical symbol $\vee$ for the "either-or" relation into the subscripts and write:

$$\left(\frac{\partial n_i}{\partial \mu_j}\right)_{(l \vee f)(n_j \vee \mu_i)} = \left(\frac{\partial n_j}{\partial \mu_i}\right)_{(l \vee f)(n_i \vee \mu_j)} \tag{17}$$

$$\left(\frac{\partial n_i}{\partial n_j}\right)_{(l\lor f)(\mu_i\lor \mu_j)} = -\left(\frac{\partial \mu_j}{\partial \mu_i}\right)_{(l\lor f)(n_j\lor n_i)} \tag{18}$$

$$\left(\frac{\partial f}{\partial n_i}\right)_{(l\lor \mu_i)(n_j\lor \mu_j)} = \left(\frac{\partial \mu_i}{\partial l}\right)_{(n_i\lor f)(n_j\lor \mu_j)} \tag{19}$$

$$\left(\frac{\partial f}{\partial \mu_i}\right)_{(l\lor n_i)(n_j\lor \mu_j)} = -\left(\frac{\partial n_i}{\partial l}\right)_{(\mu_i\lor f)(n_j\lor \mu_j)}. \tag{20}$$

The use of eqs. (17–20) may be illustrated by writing for example eq. (20) explicitly in the following four different forms:

$$\left(\frac{\partial f}{\partial \mu_i}\right)_{ln_j} = -\left(\frac{\partial n_i}{\partial l}\right)_{\mu_i n_j}; \quad \left(\frac{\partial f}{\partial \mu_i}\right)_{l\mu_j} = -\left(\frac{\partial n_i}{\partial l}\right)_{\mu_i \mu_j}$$

$$\left(\frac{\partial f}{\partial \mu_i}\right)_{n_i n_j} = -\left(\frac{\partial n_i}{\partial l}\right)_{fn_j}; \quad \left(\frac{\partial f}{\partial \mu_i}\right)_{n_i \mu_j} = -\left(\frac{\partial n_i}{\partial l}\right)_{f\mu_j}.$$

It may be noted that it is only the subscripts $l \lor f$ which distinguish eqs. (17) and (18) from corresponding equations for solutions, and determine their mechanochemical significance.

The cross-coefficients and the differential capacities may be interrelated by using the identity

$$\left(\frac{\partial x}{\partial y}\right)_z \cdot \left(\frac{\partial y}{\partial z}\right)_x \cdot \left(\frac{\partial z}{\partial x}\right)_y = -1. \tag{21}$$

For instance we may derive the chemical capacity $\partial n_i/\partial \mu_i$ from $\partial n_i/\partial l$ and $\partial \mu_i/\partial l$

$$\left(\frac{\partial n_i}{\partial \mu_i}\right)_l = -\frac{(\partial n_i/\partial l)_{\mu_i}}{(\partial \mu_i/\partial l)_{n_i}}. \tag{22}$$

Similarly, the mechanical capacity at constant n_i is given by

$$\left(\frac{\partial l}{\partial f}\right)_{n_i} = -\left(\frac{\partial l}{\partial n_i}\right)_f \left(\frac{\partial n_i}{\partial f}\right)_l \tag{23a}$$

and at constant μ_i by

$$\left(\frac{\partial l}{\partial f}\right)_{\mu_i} = -\left(\frac{\partial l}{\partial \mu_i}\right)_f \left(\frac{\partial \mu_i}{\partial f}\right)_l. \tag{23b}$$

Dividing eq. (23a) by (23b) we obtain the significant equality of the ratios of mechanical and chemical capacities,

$$\frac{(\partial l/\partial f)_{n_i}}{(\partial l/\partial f)_{\mu_i}} = \frac{(\partial n_i/\partial \mu_i)_l}{(\partial n_i/\partial \mu_i)_f}. \tag{24}$$

2.3. *Cross relations in the swelling of poly-acids*

As an example of the use of eqs. (19), (20) and (21) in the analysis of experimental results we shall consider the behaviour of contractile polyacid fibres.

It is known[16] that partially neutralized fibres contract strongly upon the addition of mineral acid (say HCl) and may lift concurrently a weight, i.e. increasing n_{HCl} in the system causes a decrease in l at constant f, or $(\partial l/\partial n_{HCl})_f < 0$. Similarly if the contractile fibre is kept at constant l the tension increases upon the addition of hydrochloric acid, or $(\partial f/\partial n_{HCl})_l > 0$. The relation between these two observations follows directly from eq. (21),

$$\left(\frac{\partial f}{\partial n_{HCl}}\right)_l = -\left(\frac{\partial l}{\partial n_{HCl}}\right)_f \cdot \left(\frac{\partial f}{\partial l}\right)_{n_{HCl}}.$$

Since for mechanical stability it is required that $(\partial f/\partial l)$ be always positive, it follows that if $(\partial l/\partial n_{HCl})_f$ is negative than $(\partial f/\partial n_{HCl})_f$ has to be positive.

Recently, Kuhn *et al.*[22] demonstrated a reverse effect: upon stretching a contractile polyacid fibre there is a measurable drop in the pH of the surrounding bath in equilibrium with the fibre. A drop in the pH is equivalent here to an increase in the chemical potential of the hydrochloric acid in the system so that Kuhn's effect can be expressed in the form $(\partial \mu_{HCl}/\partial f)_{n_{HCl}} > 0$. Regarding the gel and its bath as a single system this observation is a direct consequence of eq. (20), which may be written in the form

$$-\left(\frac{\partial l}{\partial n_{HCl}}\right)_f = \left(\frac{\partial \mu_{HCl}}{\partial f}\right)_{n_{HCl}}.$$

Since

$$-\left(\frac{\partial l}{\partial n_{HCl}}\right)_f > 0$$

it follows that

$$\left(\frac{\partial \mu_{HCl}}{\partial f}\right)_{n_{HCl}} > 0,$$

as observed by Kuhn *et al.* A more detailed analysis of the experiment based on the treatment of the equilibrium between the gel phase and surrounding medium leads to the same result. A similar observation was made by Z. Alexandrowicz of this Laboratory. He found that the pH of water in equilibrium with a partially neutralized polyacid gel increases when the gel is subjected to pressure. It may be readily shown that this phenomenon is the consequence of the corresponding cross-relation

$$\left(\frac{\partial V_{\text{gel}}}{\partial n_{\text{NaOH}}}\right)_p = \left(\frac{\partial \mu_{\text{NaOH}}}{\partial p}\right)_{n_{\text{NaOH}}}.$$

Since generally the volume of the polyacid gel increases with addition of alkali, $(\partial V/\partial n_{\text{NaOH}})_p > 0$, the potential μ of the NaOH in the medium has to rise with the application of pressure.

3. THE WORK CYCLE

3.1. *Geometrical representation of the mechanochemical behaviour*

3.1.1. Before considering the characteristics of an integral mechanochemical process it is advantageous to pay some attention to its geometrical representation. The thermodynamic geometry of our systems requires a $2s + 8$ dimensional space to describe fully the behaviour of s reactive chemical components (n_i, μ_i), the polymeric component of the working substance (n_p, μ_p), the thermal changes (T, S), the pressure–volume changes (p, V) and the contractile performance (f, l). Since the trajectory described by the process in the $2s + 8$ dimensional space is rather abstract we shall consider instead only some plane projections of the thermodynamic surface on several of the two-dimensional coordinate planes. Among all possible projection planes we choose those whose coordinates are conjugate variables, as the f–l plane or the μ_i–n_i planes. The projection of a cyclic process on these planes gives directly the energy contribution of the conjugated variables to the energy balance of the cycle. Thus the projection of a cyclic process on the f–l plane gives the mechanical work obtained in the process while any closed trajectory projected on the μ_i–n_i plane represents the contribution of the ith component to the turnover of the chemical energy.

3.1.2. For the sake of simplicity we shall consider first an engine reacting with a single chemical component, i.e. a mechanochemical system of two degrees of freedom (at constant n_p, p and T), say the stretching force f and the chemical potential μ of the reagent.

Many important characteristics will come to light already in this simple case and the generalization to a multicomponent interaction will not present fundamental difficulties.

Assume that the dependent variables, in this case the contents n of the reactive species and the length l of the fibre, were determined for all values of the two independent variables μ and f. The geometric representation of the behaviour of our system would require a two dimensional thermodynamic surface in the four dimensional space of n, μ, f and l. We now project this surface on the f–l plane. To each value of μ the f–l relation will be given by a curve which describes l as function of the independent variable f, with the independent variable μ as parameter. As n is another dependent variable its value is fixed for each point of the f–l curve. In other words to each point of the f–l plane there corresponds a single pair of μ–n values.

The curves of constant μ in the f–l plane have been designated as *isopotentials*. All points of a single isopotential curve could be readily obtained from a single stress–strain experiment carried out in a large bath of constant *chemical potential*. The reader will observe the similarity of the *isopotentials* to the *isotherms* where the mechanical changes of a thermal engine are taking place during the contact with a large reservoir of constant *thermal potential*.

The same consideration may be followed on choosing f and n as the independent variables, instead of f and μ. The family of f–l curves at constant n represents the behaviour of an isolated fibre engine loaded with constant amounts of reactive substance undergoing a stress–strain experiment. The curves of constant chemical load will be designated as *isophores*. They bear an evident similarity to the *adiabates* of a thermal engine where the amount of entropy is constant and it is the thermal potential that changes during mechanical operation.

Turning now to the projection on the μ–n plane it is clear that the isopotentials and isophores will appear as straight perpendicular lines. It is of interest however to join the projection points also by curves of either constant force f or constant fibre length l. Following the physiological terminology we shall denote curves at constant f as *isotones* and those at constant l as *isometrics*. These two families of curves, the isotones and isometrics, are related to the isopotentials and isophores and we shall subsequently show how to transfer the mechanochemical representation in the f–l plane to the corresponding representation in the μ–n plane.

3.1.3. The case of a mechanochemical engine reacting with several components may be treated similarly. Assume that the engine reacts with two components 1 and 2 to which it may be open or from which it may be isolated. As in this case the system has a variance of three (at constant p, T and n_p) its behaviour can be described fully by three equations of state. The choice of the equations of state is arbitrary provided that all the six variables (n, μ_1, n_2, μ_2, f and l) appear in the set of equations. Thus we might choose the following three equations of state

(a) $f = f(l;\ \mu_1\mu_2)$

(b) $f = f(l;\ \mu_1 n_2)$

(c) $f = f(l;\ n_1 n_2)$.

The first equation (a) represents the mechanical behaviour of an isopotential engine open to both reactive species 1 and 2 maintaining equilibrium with an external bath at chemical potentials μ_1 and μ_2. The second equation (b) represents the behaviour of a singly isolated engine, open towards component 1 and closed towards component 2. The third equation (c) represents the fully isolated, isophoric, behaviour of the engine.

Each equation of state is represented in the f–l plane by a two-parameters family of curves. Since a given point P in the f–l plane does not determine uniquely the μ_i and n_i values of the reactants, there is an infinite number of states of the system belonging to P. Therefore, an infinite number of curves of each family pass through P. However, once one parameter, say μ_1, is specified all three curves ($\mu_1\mu_2$), ($\mu_1 n_2$) and ($n_1 n_2$) through P are uniquely determined.

3.2. *The integral mechanochemical cycle*

3.2.1. The consideration of closed reversible work cycles has the advantage that it brings to light the capacity of the engine to transform chemical into mechanical energy, since after the cycle is completed, the net amount of work performed by the engine must be balanced by changes in the external sources of chemical energy. Integrating the Gibbs equation (eq. 2) for the mechanochemical engine (not including the external sources) over a complete cycle at constant temperature and pressure we have

$$\oint dU = T\oint dS - p\oint dV + \oint f dl + \sum_i \oint \mu_i dn_i \qquad (25)$$

and observing that the integrals of all state functions are zero in a cycle, we get

$$\oint f dl = \sum_i -\mu_i dn_i \qquad (26)$$

In the elementary arbitrary mechanochemical step (eq. 2) the entry of chemical energy ($\sum \mu_i dn_i$) into the engine is accompanied not

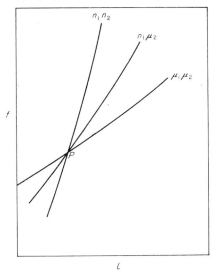

FIG. 1. A pure isopotential $\mu_1 \mu_2$, a pure isophore $n_1 n_2$, and a mixed isopotential–isophore $\mu_2 n_1$, with the same values of $\mu_1 \mu_2 n_1 n_2$ at their common intersection point P.

only by the performance of mechanical work ($f dl$); superimposed on it are also the change in thermal energy (TdS), compressional work ($-p dV$) and changes in internal energy (dU) which obscure the pure mechanochemical relation. In a closed cycle, however, at constant T and p these terms cancel out and the pure mechanochemical relation is clearly manifested. At the end of the cycle the engine returns to its original state ($\oint dU = 0$) and the mechanical and chemical changes will be found in the external world.

Equation (26) demonstrates that in order to get mechanical work there should exist a gradient of the chemical potential of at least one reactive substance in the surroundings of the engine. In other words a contractile system cannot operate cyclically on account of a reservoir of constant chemical potentials of all the reactive species. This is the mechanochemical equivalent of Kelvin's principle that no thermal engine can operate cyclically on the account of a reservoir of constant temperature.

3.2.2. The simplest scheme of a mechanochemical cycle is that of an engine operating between two reservoirs of chemical potentials $\mu^I \neq \mu^{II}$ for one reactive component. In terms of geometrical

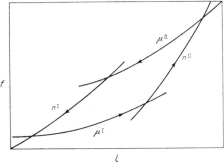

FIG. 2. A four stroke cycle with a single reactive component, consisting of two isopotentials μ^I, μ^{II} and two isophores n^I, n^{II}.

representation discussed in 3.1.2 this would mean that the engine operates between two isopotentials.

For this case we divide the cycle into four strokes (Fig. 2): during two strokes the engine maintains contact with the reservoirs and exchanges matter with the surroundings ($dn \neq 0$) while in the other two strokes of the cycle the engine is isolated and $dn = 0$. The process may now be described as follows

$$W = -\oint f dl = \int_I \mu dn + \int_{II} \mu dn$$
$$= \mu^I \int_I dn + \mu^{II} \int_{II} dn = (\mu^I - \mu^{II}) \, \Delta n. \qquad (27)$$

Thus the mechanical work is given by the product of chemical potential difference and the amount Δn of reactive substance transported in the cycle,

$$\left(\Delta n = \int_I dn = - \int_{II} dn\right).$$

It is worth mentioning the analogy between the mechano-chemical cycle and the classical Carnot cycle. The Carnot cycle is derived from the Gibbs equation for the case that the only changes in the engine are compressional work and entropy transport, i.e. when $dU = TdS - pdV$. On cyclic integration one gets

$$\oint dU = 0 = \oint TdS - \oint pdV.$$

If the operation is carried out between two reservoirs of thermal potentials T_1 and T_2 one gets directly the well known expression

$$W = \oint pdV = (T_1 - T_2)\,\Delta S. \tag{28}$$

The thermal efficiency $\eta = (T_1 - T_2)/T_1$ has no counterpart in mechanochemistry since the chemical potential has no absolute zero; therefore the ratio of the work obtained in a cycle with a single reactive component to the "work" introduced at the higher potential $(\mu^I - \mu^{II})\,\Delta n/\mu^I \Delta n$, depends on the reference state chosen for μ. On the other hand the work coefficient η' defined as the ratio of the work obtained in a real cycle to that expected in a reversible cyclic process is significant also for the characterization of real mechano-chemical cycles,

$$\eta' = - \oint f dl / \sum_i \oint \mu_i dn_i, \tag{29}$$

where the numerator and the denominator express respectively the work and the chemical change in the external world.

3.2.3. If the engine operates on account of several reactive components whose chemical potentials are maintained at different levels in the two reservoirs, then the work performed will be given by the sum of the products:

$$W = \sum_i (\mu_i^I - \mu_i^{II})\,\Delta n_i. \tag{30}$$

It should be emphasized that in the polycomponent case reversible performance can generally not be realized in a four stroke cycle. Let us consider an engine taking up all the components contained in a given reservoir in a fully isopotential stroke. The engine is then isolated from this reservoir, and further strained in a fully isophoric stroke. The chemical potentials of the components absorbed in the fibre will change, therefore, in a way characteristic of the engine. It is generally possible to adjust another reservoir to be in equilibrium with the engine at the end of the isophoric change. (Usually such an adjustment will require the introduction of a non-transferable component to satisfy the Gibbs–Duhem equation for the reservoir.) A second isopotential stroke may now be performed with the engine maintaining equilibrium with the second reservoir. In this stroke the different components will as a rule not be released (or taken up) in the same rate as in the first isopotential. Hence, in general, it is impossible to revert in the second fully isopotential stroke to the initial n_i values of the components in the engine. In other words the second isopotential does not necessarily possess any point from which the system might be reverted to its initial state along a fully isophoric stroke. While a polycomponent engine cannot therefore be operated usually in a four stroke cycle, a closed cycle may be obtained with more than four strokes, if suitable isolating mechanisms are introduced.

4. ELEMENTARY CYCLES AND CRITERIA OF MECHANOCHEMICAL COUPLING

The thermodynamic relations between the mechanical performance and the chemical turnover, presented in the previous chapter, are of a general nature and valid for any possible mechanochemical system. They do not give however detailed information on the specific properties of a system under consideration, and therefore do not provide suitable criteria for the distinction between more favourable and less favourable mechanochemical performance. In the present chapter we shall propose criteria by which the adequacy of a system for mechanochemical performance can be characterized by a number of differential capacities and cross-coefficients. We shall discuss first the case of an engine reacting with a single component. Subsequently we shall consider the case of two or more reactive species.

4.1. *The efficacy of a mechanochemical engine*

The criteria for mechanochemical performance are of two kinds, the one being dependent on the mechanical properties of the working substance of the engine, and the other on its chemical properties. We shall first describe the two criteria and then show their equivalence.

4.1.1. The mechanical properties of a mechanochemical engine are completely represented by the familes of isophores and iso-potentials in the f–l plane. The slopes $(\partial f/\partial l)_n$ and $(\partial f/dl)_\mu$ at any given point P in the f–l plane are properties of the substance of the engine at that point, if f and l are taken as *reduced quantities* (f is force per unit of an initial cross section, and l is extension per an initial unit length). In fact $(\partial f/\partial l)_n$ and $(\partial f/\partial l)_\mu$ as reduced quantities are the Young's moduli of the substance under isophoric and iso-potential extensions respectively.

The work performed by an elementary isophoric–isopotential cycle around the point P is represented by the area of the parallelo-gram enclosed between two adjacent isophores and two adjacent isopotentials (Fig. 4).

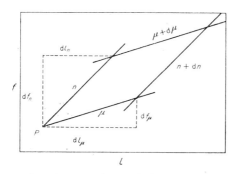

FIG. 3.   Elementary isophoric–isopotential cycle.

The area is different from zero if, and only if, the slopes of the iso-phores and isopotentials do not coincide. It is therefore a necessary and sufficient condition for mechanochemical performance that the engine substance possess two distinct extension coefficients. We may taken the difference ϵ_1 between these coefficients

$$\epsilon_1 = \left(\frac{\partial f}{\partial l}\right)_n - \left(\frac{\partial f}{\partial l}\right)_\mu \tag{31}$$

as a measure of the feasibility of mechanochemical operation of the system at the point P. This difference can never be negative, accord-ing to the second law of thermodynamics, as seen from the following considerations.

Assume that an engine, initially at length l_0 and force f_0 in equilibrium with a reservoir of a reactive species, is isolated and stretched isophorically by a finite length Δl with an expenditure of work $(\Delta W)_n$. If $(\partial f/\partial l)_n$ and $(\partial f/\partial l)_\mu$ are different, then the engine will get out of equilibrium with the reservoir upon the isophoric stretching. Now let us re-establish the contact with the reservoir, keeping l constant. The result must be an irreversible spontaneous process which will bring the engine to a position on the isopotential curve which passes through the initial point. If we go now back to the initial state isopotentially, we shall recover only part of the work $(\Delta W)_n$, i.e. $(\Delta W)_\mu \leqslant (\Delta W)_n$ for a given extension Δl. This implies

$$\left(\frac{\partial f}{\partial l}\right)_n - \left(\frac{\partial f}{\partial l}\right)_\mu \geqslant 0 \qquad (32)$$

because, neglecting terms of second and higher orders, we have

$$(\Delta W)_n = f_0 \Delta l + \tfrac{1}{2}\left(\frac{\partial f}{\partial l}\right)_n (\Delta l)^2$$

$$(\Delta W)_\mu = f_0 \Delta l + \tfrac{1}{2}\left(\frac{\partial f}{\partial l}\right)_\mu (\Delta l)^2$$

therefore

$$(\Delta W)_n - (\Delta W)_\mu = \tfrac{1}{2}\left[\left(\frac{\partial f}{\partial l}\right)_n - \left(\frac{\partial f}{\partial l}\right)_{\mu}\right](\Delta l)^2 \geqslant 0. \qquad (33)$$

4.1.2. Turning now our attention to the chemical aspect of the process we shall consider the ability of the engine to transfer reversibly a chemical reagent from one reservoir to another, the reservoir being at different chemical potentials. This ability depends on two properties:

(a) The ability of the engine to absorb (or liberate) an amount of reactant by a dimensional change during an isopotential process. The quantitative measure of this property is the *isopotential coupling* or *isopotential cross-coefficient* $(\partial n/\partial l)_\mu$. Here n and l are again reduced quantities (n is the number of moles of reactant per an initial unit volume of the engine, and l is the extension per an initial unit length).

(b) The ability to change the chemical potential of the reactant during an isophoric process. The measure of this property is the *isophoric coupling coefficient* $(\partial \mu/\partial l)_n$.

The vanishing of either of these coefficients will evidently make a mechanochemical cycle impossible; on the other hand, the larger the product of these coefficients the larger will be the amount of turnover of chemical energy per units of extension in both the isophoric and isopotential steps.

We may therefore take the product

$$\epsilon_2 = - \left(\frac{\partial n}{\partial l}\right)_\mu \left(\frac{\partial \mu}{\partial l}\right)_n \qquad (34'.$$

as an alternative measure of the mechanochemical adequacy of a system. The minus sign is introduced in order to make the product non-negative, since the product $(\partial n/\partial l)_\mu (\partial \mu/\partial l)_n$ is always negative or zero. To prove this we apply the identity

$$\left(\frac{\partial \mu}{\partial l}\right)_n = - \left(\frac{\partial n}{\partial l}\right)_\mu \left(\frac{\partial \mu}{\partial n}\right)_l \qquad (35)$$

which corresponds to the general relation given in eq. (21). Since $(\partial \mu/\partial n)_l$ is always positive for stable thermodynamic systems, $(\partial \mu/\partial l)_n$ and $(\partial n/\partial l)_\mu$ must have opposite signs.

4.1.3. Hitherto we have introduced four coefficients which characterize the mechanochemical behaviour. We have proposed either the difference of the mechanical coefficients (eq. 31), or the product of the coupling coefficients (eq. 34) as a measure of the adequacy of a system to serve as a mechanochemical engine. We shall show now that these two measures are identical, i.e. that the following significant relation holds

$$\left(\frac{\partial f}{\partial l}\right)_n - \left(\frac{\partial f}{\partial l}\right)_\mu = - \left(\frac{\partial \mu}{\partial l}\right)_n \left(\frac{\partial n}{\partial l}\right)_\mu \geqslant 0. \qquad (36)$$

Since the engine system with a single chemical reactive species is a bivariant system (at constant p, T and n_p), we have

$$df = \left(\frac{\partial f}{\partial l}\right)_\mu dl + \left(\frac{\partial f}{\partial \mu}\right)_l d\mu \qquad (37)$$

and therefore

$$\left(\frac{\partial f}{\partial l}\right)_n = \left(\frac{\partial f}{\partial l}\right)_\mu + \left(\frac{\partial f}{\partial \mu}\right)_l \left(\frac{\partial \mu}{\partial l}\right)_n. \qquad (38)$$

Equation (36) is obtained from eq. (38) by applying the cross relation $(\partial f/\partial \mu)_l = - (\partial n/\partial l)_\mu$ (cf. eq. 20). Thus both ϵ_1 and ϵ_2 (eqs. 31

and 34) give the same measure for the adequacy of mechano-chemical performance. We denote this measure by ϵ and propose to call it *efficacy*. The dimension of the efficacy is energy per unit volume. It represents the useful work (per unit initial volume of the fibre-engine) obtained in a complete elementary cycle per units of reduced extensions in both the isophoric and isopotential steps.

4.1.4. Alternatively, it is possible to choose the coefficients of the isotonic–isometric cycle in the μ–n plane to obtain another measure of mechanochemical adequacy. It is given either by the difference between the isometric and the isotonic slopes

$$\eta_1 = \left(\frac{\partial \mu}{\partial n}\right)_l - \left(\frac{\partial \mu}{\partial n}\right)_f \geqslant 0, \tag{39}$$

or by the product

$$\eta_2 = -\left(\frac{\partial l}{\partial n}\right)_f \left(\frac{\partial f}{\partial n}\right)_l. \tag{40}$$

The equality of η_1 and η_2 may be shown in analogy to the proof of eq. (36). Thus we have

$$\eta = \left(\frac{\partial \mu}{\partial n}\right)_l - \left(\frac{\partial \mu}{\partial n}\right)_f = -\left(\frac{\partial l}{\partial n}\right)_f \left(\frac{\partial f}{\partial n}\right)_l. \tag{41}$$

The dimension of η is energy $\times$ volume.

4.1.5. A comparison of eqs. (36) and (41) as well as the discussion in chapter 3 reveal clearly the complementary nature of the isophoric–isopotential cycle and the isometric–isotonic cycle. It is therefore natural to consider the value of η defined by eq. (41) as the *isometric–isotonic efficacy* of a system. It is easy to verify that two different fibre engines may have the same efficacy ϵ without having the same η.

A third measure of mechanochemical adequacy may be defined as the ratio ρ,

$$\rho = \frac{\epsilon}{(\partial f/\partial l)_n}, \tag{42}$$

which will be termed the *mechanochemical ratio*. Since by eq. (36) $\sim \geqslant \epsilon \geqslant 0$, we see that

$$l \geqslant \rho \geqslant 0. \tag{43}$$

The extreme value $\rho = 0$ is obtained only when $\epsilon = 0$, i.e. when the system is non-mechanochemical. The upper limit is obtained when either $(\partial f/\partial l)_n \rightarrow \sim$ or $(\partial f/\partial l)_\mu \rightarrow 0$.

The mechanochemical ratio may be related also to the isometric–isotonic efficacy η in the following way. From eq. (24) we have

$$\frac{(\partial f/\partial l)_\mu}{(\partial f/\partial l)_n} = \frac{(\partial \mu/\partial n)_f}{(\partial \mu/\partial n)_l} = l - \rho \tag{44}$$

and therefore

$$\rho = \frac{\eta}{(\partial \mu/\partial n)_l}. \tag{45}$$

It is seen that the mechanochemical ratio is related to the isophoric–isopotential cycle and to the isometric–isotonic cycle in a similar manner. This together with its being a dimensionless quantity, renders it a useful parameter for mechanochemical characterization.

The mechanochemical ratio ρ is analogous to the ratio between the heat capacities at constant pressure and constant volume, $\gamma = c_p/c_V$. Replacing in eq. (24) f and l by $-p$ and V, μ and n by T and S we may write down the following relation

$$\frac{(\partial P/\partial V)_T}{(\partial P/\partial V)_S} = \frac{T(\partial S/\partial T)_V}{T(\partial S/\partial T)_p} = \frac{c_V}{c_p} = \gamma^{-1}, \tag{46}$$

which states that the ratio between the slopes of the isotherm and the adiabate in the p–V plane is given by γ^{-1}. The analogous ratio between the slopes of the isopotential and isophore in the f–l plane is given by $l - \rho$. Thus ρ is the mechanochemical analogue of $(\gamma - 1)/\gamma$.

4.2. *Transformations of elementary cycles and mechanochemical criteria*

4.2.1. In Section 3 we have discussed the geometric representation of a mechanochemical system by applying the projection of its representative surface on the f–l and the μ–n planes. Now we wish to describe the correlation between the chemical and mechanical properties through the one–one correspondence of the points in the μ–n plane and the f–l plane, which exists for systems with a single reactive component. This correspondence will be given as a linear transformation of the infinitesimal region around a point in the μ–n plane onto its corresponding region in the f–l plane.

Let P be a point in the f–l plane with the reduced quantities and l as coordinates. An infinitesimal displacement $dP = (df, dl)$ is given as a function of the corresponding displacement $d\pi = (d\mu, dn)$ in the μ–n plane by the equation

$$df = \left(\frac{\partial f}{\partial \mu}\right)_n d\mu + \left(\frac{\partial f}{\partial n}\right)_\mu dn,$$

$$dl = \left(\frac{\partial l}{\partial \mu}\right)_n d\mu + \left(\frac{\partial l}{\partial n}\right)_\mu dn. \tag{47}$$

The four transformation coefficients $(\partial f/\partial \mu)_n$, etc., form the elements of the transformation matrix which represents the one–one correspondence between the two regions. In the formalism of matrix algebra eq. (47) may be written as

$$\begin{pmatrix} df \\ dl \end{pmatrix} = \begin{pmatrix} \left(\dfrac{\partial f}{\partial \mu}\right)_n & \left(\dfrac{\partial f}{\partial n}\right)_\mu \\ \left(\dfrac{\partial l}{\partial \mu}\right)_n & \left(\dfrac{\partial l}{\partial n}\right)_\mu \end{pmatrix} \begin{pmatrix} d\mu \\ dn \end{pmatrix}. \tag{48}$$

These four coefficients are functions of the location of P in the f–l plane (or alternatively, of the point π in the μ–n plane). They characterize the mechanochemical properties of a system, serving thus the same purpose as the four coefficients $(\partial f/\partial l)_n$, $(\partial f/\partial l)$, $(\partial \mu/\partial l)_n$, $(\partial n/\partial l)$ considered in Section 4.1. We shall next see how the transformation coefficients are related to the vertices of elementary work-parallelogram and derive a relation between them, equivalent to eq. (36).

4.2.2. Let us consider the elementary rectangle in the μ–n plane describing an infinitesimal cycle between two adjacent isophores and two adjacent isopotentials. The area of the rectangle, $d\mu dn$ is equal to the chemical energy expended by the transfer of an amount dn of the reactant across a chemical potential difference $d\mu$. The image of this rectangle in the f–l plane is the parallelogram which describes the same cycle in the f–l plane, and its area represents the work done by the engine during this cycle.

Let the displacements along the isophore and the isopotential through P be denoted by (df_n, dl_n) and (df_μ, dl_μ) respectively (Fig. 3). According to eq. (47) these are given by

$$df_n = \left(\frac{\partial f}{\partial \mu}\right)_n d\mu \qquad df_\mu = \left(\frac{\partial f}{\partial n}\right)_\mu dn \left.\begin{array}{c} \\ \\ \\ \\ \end{array}\right\}$$

$$dl_n = \left(\frac{\partial l}{\partial \mu}\right)_n d\mu \qquad dl = \left(\frac{\partial l}{\partial n}\right)_\mu dn. \qquad (49)$$

The area of the parallelogram dW is given, according to a well-known theorem in analytical geometry, by the determinant

$$dW = \left\| \begin{array}{cc} df_n & df_\mu \\ dl_n & dl_\mu \end{array} \right\|. \qquad (50)$$

Inserting eqs. (49) we obtain

$$dW = \left\| \begin{array}{cc} \left(\dfrac{\partial f}{\partial \mu}\right)_n & \left(\dfrac{\partial f}{\partial n}\right)_\mu \\ \left(\dfrac{\partial l}{\partial \mu}\right)_n & \left(\dfrac{\partial l}{\partial n}\right)_\mu \end{array} \right\| d\mu dn = D\, d\mu dn, \qquad (51)$$

where D is seen to be the determinant of the transformation matrix (eq. 48). According to eq. (26), the sum of the areas dW and $d\mu dn$ must vanish

$$dW + d\mu dn = 0, \qquad (52)$$

hence the value of D is -1, i.e.

$$\left(\frac{\partial f}{\partial \mu}\right)_n \left(\frac{\partial l}{\partial n}\right)_\mu - \left(\frac{\partial f}{\partial n}\right)_\mu \left(\frac{\partial l}{\partial \mu}\right)_n = -1. \qquad (53)$$

This relation between the four transformation coefficients is equivalent to eq. (36), and shows that the number of independent differential coefficients necessary for the characterization of mechanochemical system is 3.

The equivalence of eqs. (36) and (53) can be seen as follows. Inserting the identities

3

$$\left(\frac{\partial f}{\partial \mu}\right)_n = \left(\frac{\partial f}{\partial l}\right)_n \left(\frac{\partial l}{\partial \mu}\right)_n \left.\vphantom{\begin{array}{c}1\\1\\1\end{array}}\right\}$$

$$\left(\frac{\partial f}{\partial n}\right)_\mu = \left(\frac{\partial f}{\partial l}\right)_\mu \left(\frac{\partial l}{\partial n}\right)_\mu$$

(54)

in eq. (53) we obtain

$$\left(\frac{\partial l}{\partial \mu}\right)_n \left(\frac{\partial l}{\partial n}\right)_\mu \left[\left(\frac{\partial f}{\partial l}\right)_n - \left(\frac{\partial f}{\partial l}\right)_\mu\right] = -1 \qquad (55)$$

or

$$\left(\frac{\partial f}{\partial l}\right)_n - \left(\frac{\partial f}{\partial l}\right)_\mu = -\left(\frac{\partial \mu}{\partial l}\right)_n \left(\frac{\partial n}{\partial l}\right)_\mu$$

which is eq. (36).

The equivalence of eqs. (41) and (43) can be shown in a similar way.

4.2.3. Consider a family of elementary cycles in the f–l plane at a given point P, with a common isophore and a variable isopotential slope $(\partial f/\partial l)_\mu$. When the isopotential slope tends to zero, the efficacy of the cycle increases to the limit $\epsilon_0 = (\partial f/\partial l)_n$ and the mechanochemical ratio tends to unity. The limiting cycle with $(\partial f/\partial l)_\mu = 0$ corresponds to a cycle with an isopotential phase transition taking place in the fibre engine. A detailed discussion of this case was given by Flory et al.[23] who pointed out that "such a mechanical-chemical system, since it depends on phase transition, should be a far more sensitive converter of chemical to mechanical energy than the much-discussed polyelectrolyte systems which give rise to relatively low isotropic forces of osmotic origin". Using our criteria it can be stated that a cycle with isopotential phase transition has maximal efficacy among all cycles with a common isophore, and its mechanochemical ratio is maximal ($\rho = 1$) irrespective of the value of the isophoric slope.

In view of these considerations ρ may be given the following simple geometrical interpretation: the area of the obliquely shaded elementary cycle in Fig. 4 is given by eq. (51). The area dW_0^I of the limiting cycle of the family with $(\partial f/\partial l)_\mu = 0$ (horizontally shaded) is given by

$$dW_0^I = \left\| \begin{array}{cc} df_n & 0 \\ dl_n & dl_\mu \end{array} \right\| = \left(\frac{\partial f}{\partial \mu}\right)_n \left(\frac{\partial l}{\partial n}\right)_\mu d\mu dn. \qquad (56)$$

It can be readily verified that ρ is the ratio of the two areas

$$\rho = \frac{\mathrm{d}W}{\mathrm{d}W_0}. \tag{57}$$

Consider now another family of elementary cycles at the point P, with a common isopotential and a variable isophoric slcpe $(\partial f/\partial l)_n$. When the isophoric slope goes to infinity the efficacy too tends to infinity while the mechanochemical ratio tends to unity. Here the limiting case $(\partial f/\partial l)_n = \sim$ represents an engine with pure chemical elasticity, i.e. in this case dimensional changes occur only upon take-up or

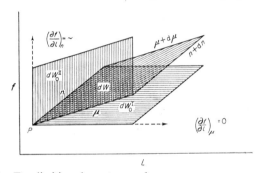

FIG. 4.   Two limiting elementary cycles:
  I with isopotential phase transition,
  II with chemical elasticity, corresponding to a given elementary cycle.

release of the reactant. This limiting elementary cycle is represented in Fig. 4 by the vertically shaded area $\mathrm{d}W_0^{II}$, and is given by

$$\mathrm{d}W_0^{II} = \left\| \begin{array}{cc} \mathrm{d}f_n & \mathrm{d}f_\mu \\ 0 & \mathrm{d}l_\mu \end{array} \right\|. \tag{58}$$

Evidently, $\mathrm{d}W_0^{II} = \mathrm{d}W_0^I$ hence ρ may be interpreted also as the ratio $\mathrm{d}W/\mathrm{d}W_0^{II}$.

4.2.4. In concluding the discussion of elementary cycles with a single reactive component we would like to stress the independence of the three criteria ϵ, η and ρ. It was shown already in Section 4.2.2 that the four coefficients of the transformation matrix (eq. 48) determine a one–one correspondence between the f–l and μ–n projections and therefore characterize fully the nature of the mechanochemical cycle of a system at each point. It was also pointed out that through eq. (53) the number of independent differential coefficients is reduced to 3. The choice of the criteria ϵ, η and ρ is equivalent to the selection of any three independent differential coefficients which are necessary and sufficient to characterize the mechanochemical elementary cycle.

4.3. *Mechanochemical coupling in polycomponent systems*

In the previous sections of this chapter we observed that the existence of two different Young's moduli is a necessary condition for mechanochemical performance in engines with a single reactant. Furthermore, we determined certain relations between these mechanical coefficients and several mechanochemical coupling-coefficients. In the case of mechanochemical systems with several reactants the number of different Young's moduli and the number of conditions for mechanochemical performance increase considerably with the number of reactive components and with the number of possible restrictions on permeability. In the present section we discuss some aspects of the mechanochemical coupling in systems with several reactive components. We generalize the inequality relation (eq. 32) between the mechanical coefficients of single reactant systems, as well as the relation (eq. 36) between these coefficients and the mechanochemical cross-coefficients $(\partial n_i/\partial l)$ and $(\partial \mu_i/\partial l)$ at various restrictive conditions.

4.3.1. Assume that the force f and the length l of the fibre engine can be changed at either constant μ_i (isopotentially) or constant n_i (isophorically) for each of the s permeable components. In general for each set of such specified conditions of permeability there will exist a different mechanical coefficient $\partial f/\partial l$. The system may therefore have up to 2^s Young's moduli. The existence of differences between these mechanical coefficients permits the construction of mechanochemical cycles and, as in the case of a single reactant, provides quantitative measures of mechanochemical feasibility, or *efficacy*.

We shall now examine the differences between mechanical coefficients at different degrees of isolation. For this purpose we arrange the curves passing through a point P in the f–l plane in series, each consecutive curve in a series having one isolation less than the previous curve. Thus, starting with the curve for fully isophoric conditions (constant $n_1 n_2 n_3 \ldots n_s$ or in short $\mathbf{n}^s$), we choose as second in this series an $f\text{–}l$ curve at constant $\mu_1 n_2 n_3 \ldots n_s$ (or in short $\boldsymbol{\mu}^1 \mathbf{n}^{s-1}$), then a curve at constant $\mu_1 \mu_2 n_3 \ldots n_s$ (or $\boldsymbol{\mu}^2 \mathbf{n}^{s-2}$) etc. The last in the series is the fully isopotential curve (constant $\mu_1 \mu_2 \ldots \mu_s$ or $\boldsymbol{\mu}^s$). The number of such series of consecutive curves is $s!$, each series being characterized by the order in which the isolations for the different components are being removed.

Any two *consecutive* curves in a series have equal restrictions for all the components except one. As regards this latter component, one of the two curves is its isophores, while the other curve is its isopotential. The difference between the slopes of such two consecutive curves gives the efficacy of an elementary cycle in which only one component is mechanochemically *active* being transferred from one chemical potential to another, while the other *passive* components are either isolated or maintained at constant potentials throughout the cycle.

For such polycomponent systems with a single *active* component, all the results obtained in the previous sections for single reactant systems are valid, including the various criteria of mechanochemical feasibility. Thus, for example, the efficacy ϵ_i of the single active component i is according to the present notation

$$
\begin{aligned}
\epsilon_i &= \left(\frac{\partial f}{\partial l}\right)_{\mu^{i-1} \, \mathbf{n}^{s-i+1}} - \left(\frac{\partial f}{\partial l}\right)_{\mu^i \, \mathbf{n}^{s-i}} \\
&= -\left(\frac{\partial \mu_i}{\partial l}\right)_{\mu^{i-1} \, \mathbf{n}^{s-i+1}} \left(\frac{\partial n_i}{\partial l}\right)_{\mu^i \, \mathbf{n}^{s-i}} \geqslant 0
\end{aligned}
\right\} \tag{59}
$$

corresponding to eq. (36) for a single reactant system. The slopes of the isopotentials and isophores of the active component as well as all other differential coefficients will depend in general on the values of the constant μ_i or n_i of the passive components.

4.3.2. Since each $f\text{–}l$ curve in a series of curves with consecutively decreasing isolation is an isopotential to the preceding curve and an isophore to the succeeding curve, it follows from eq. (59) that

$$
\left(\frac{\partial f}{\partial l}\right)_{\mathbf{n}^s} \geqslant \left(\frac{\partial f}{\partial l}\right)_{\mu^1 \, \mathbf{n}^{s-1}} \cdots \geqslant \left(\frac{\partial f}{\partial l}\right)_{\mu^i \, \mathbf{n}^{s-i}} \cdots \geqslant \left(\frac{\partial f}{\partial l}\right)_{\mu^s}. \tag{60}
$$

These inequalities show that the farther two curves are from each other along the series, the higher is the efficacy of an elementary cycle enclosed between them. Let us denote the efficacy of such a cycle enclosed between the ith and jth curves $(i < j)$ by ϵ_{ij}. From eq. (59) we have

$$
\begin{aligned}
\epsilon_{ij} &\equiv \left(\frac{\partial f}{\partial l}\right)_{\mu^{j-1}\, n^{s-j+1}} - \left(\frac{\partial f}{\partial l}\right)_{\mu^{i}\, n^{s-s}} \\
&= \sum_{\sigma=i}^{j} \epsilon_{\sigma} = - \sum_{\sigma=i}^{j} \left(\frac{\partial \mu_{\sigma}}{\partial l}\right)_{\mu^{\sigma-1}\, n^{s-\sigma+1}} \left(\frac{\partial n_{\sigma}}{\partial l}\right)_{\mu^{\sigma}\, n^{s-\sigma}}.
\end{aligned}
\tag{61}
$$

This equation is a generalization of eq. (36) for the case of several reactive components. It is, however, not the only possible generalization. For example, it can be shown, by writing eq. (37) for a poly-component system and applying eq. (20), that

$$
\epsilon_{ij} = - \sum_{\sigma=i}^{j} \left(\frac{\partial \mu_{\sigma}}{\partial l}\right)_{\mu^{i-1}\, n^{s-i+1}} \left(\frac{\partial n_{\sigma}}{\partial l}\right)_{\mu^{j}\, n^{s-j}}.
\tag{62}
$$

Here the constant parameters are the same for all terms on the right hand side of the equation.

A similar generalization of eq. (41) and (42) leads to pertinent expressions for isotonic–isometric efficacies η_{ij} and mechano-chemical ratios ρ_{ij} of polycomponent systems.

5. AN EXAMPLE:
THE ANALYSIS OF THE AUTONE MODEL

5.1. *The "autone" model*

5.1.1. As an example for the application of the theoretical analysis developed above we shall discuss the mechanochemical properties of a specific system. A model is chosen for the characterization instead of a set of experimental data since a model can provide all the necessary information which is only partially available for real systems both natural and synthetic. The present analysis might induce further experimental work which will lead to a deeper understanding of real systems.

The model considered here is the "autone" model developed by Gergely and Laki,[19] Polissar[20] and Hill[21] for muscular contraction. We make use of the equations of state derived by Hill for an autone with a single reactant.

5.1.2. The fibre model investigated by Hill is a macromolecular chain consisting of B units or autones, which may exist in either an extended (relaxed) state a or in a contracted state β. The length l of the chain varies between the fully extended l_{max} and the fully contracted l_{min}. In order to obtain force and length in reduced quantities we consider not a single chain but an array of A parallel chains perpendicular to the base of a parallelopiped whose constant cross section is 1 cm^2 and whose length in the contracted (initial) state is 1 cm.

Each autone has x reactive sites which may be partially occupied by a reactant taken up from an external bath. Thus the total chemical capacity of the reference parallelopiped is $x \, ABN_0^{-1}$ moles/cm^3 where N_0 is Avogadro's number. The chemical potential of the equilibrium bath is $\mu = \mu^0 + RT \ln c$ where c denotes the concentration or activity of the permeable reactant. The binding of the reactant by an autone is governed by two different equilibrium constants K_α and K_β for the two respective states of the autone. The degrees of binding in the states a and β, denoted by a and b respectively, are functions of the chemical potential or concentration of the reactant,

$$a = \frac{K_\alpha c}{1 + K_\alpha c}; \quad b = \frac{K_\beta c}{1 + K_\beta c}.$$

Hill's first equation of state relates the number of moles of reactant n absorbed by cm^3 of contractile matter to its length l and to the reactant's chemical potential μ (through a and b)

$$n = \frac{x \, AB}{N_0} \frac{a \, (l - l_{min}) + b \, (l_{max} - l)}{l_{max} \, l_{min}}. \tag{a}$$

The second equation of state relates f, l and μ.

$$f = \frac{AB \cdot RT}{N_0 \, (l_{max} - l_{min})} \left[\ln \frac{l - l_{min}}{l_{max} - l} + x \ln \frac{1 - a}{1 - b} + \text{const.} \right]. \tag{b}$$

Equations (a) and (b) will be used for the evaluation of the set of mechanochemical coefficients of the autone model. For the sake of numerical and graphical representation we assume that the number of reactive sites per 1 cm^3 of initial (contracted) fibre is

$$x \, AB \, N_0^{-1} = 2 \times 10^{-3} \text{ moles/cm}^3$$

and that the number of reactive sites per autone is $x = 2$. A contracting agent requires $K_\beta > K_\alpha$ and here we assume $K_\beta = 5 K_\alpha$. The additive constant in eq. (b) is assumed to be zero and l_{max} is taken to be 3 cm while l_{min} is 1 cm. It should be noted that l_{max} and l_{min} serve at the same time as reduced quantities 3 and 1 respectively.

Substituting the numerical values into eqs. (a) and (b) we get

$$n = 10^{-3} [a (l - 1) + b (3 - l)] \text{ mol/cm}^3 \qquad \text{(a')}$$

$$f = 1 \cdot 2 \left[\ln \frac{l - 1}{3 - l} + 2 \ln \frac{1 - a}{1 - b} \right] \text{ joule/cm}^3 \qquad \text{(b')}$$

or

$$f = 27 \left[\log \frac{l - 1}{3 - l} + 2 \log \frac{1 - a}{1 - b} \right] \text{ kg/cm}^2.$$

5.1.3. The geometrical representation of eqs. (a') and (b') in the f–l plane is given in Fig. 5. The thin lines of this figure are the isopotentials obtained by applying eq. (b') to a series of constant values of $K_\alpha c$ or corresponding values of $\log (1 - a)/(1 - b)$. The heavier and steeper lines are the isophores, obtained by graphical elimination of a and b from eqs. (a') and (b').

It will be observed that the range of existence of the mechanochemical system is limited by the boundary curves corresponding to the isopotentials of $c = 0$ and $c = \sim$. Approaching these limits the isophores merge gradually with the isopotentials and mechanochemical feasibility reduces to zero. The isophores approach the isopotentials at all concentrations also when the length of the fibre engine tends to its extreme values l_{min} and l_{max}.

The corresponding projection of the mechanochemical surface on the μ–n plane is given in Fig. 6, which represents a set of isotonic and isometric curves.

In accord with the theoretical requirement the slope of the isotone at each point is higher than that of the isometric. The region of mechanochemical performance in the μ–n plane is delimited by the isometrics $l_{max} = 3$ and $l_{min} = 1$ and by the lowest and highest contents of reactant in the engine $n = 0$ and $n = 2 \cdot 10^{-3}$ moles/cm³. The isometrics merge gradually with the isotones when the limiting lengths and limiting reactant contents are approached, indicating that chemical transformation cannot take place in the engine under these extreme conditions.

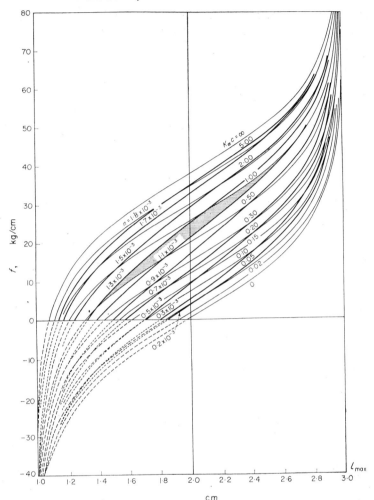

Fig. 5. Isopotentials (thin lines) and isophores (heavy lines) of the autone model in the f–l plane; c—concentration of the reactant; n—number of moles of reactant absorbed per cm³ of initial engine volume. Dotted lines indicated compression ($f < 0$).

5.2. *Application of mechanochemical criteria to the model*

5.2.1. As pointed out in the previous chapter, a characterization of the mechanochemical behaviour requires three different measures or criteria, which may be chosen in a large number of ways from the various differential capacities and coupling coefficients. In choosing such criteria for the autone model we shall take advantage of the simple features of eqs. (a) and (b) from which the various differential capacities are derived.

As the first criterium we shall take the coupling coefficient $- (\partial n/\partial l)_\mu$ which measures the change of the content of the reactant with the length of the fibre during an isopotential step. It is one of the basic properties of the autone model that the coupling coefficient

$$\left(\frac{\partial n}{\partial l}\right)_\mu = \frac{x\,AB}{N_0\,(l_{max} - l_{min})}\,(a - b) \qquad (c)$$

is a function of the chemical potential of the reactant and is independent of the degree of stretching of the engine. Figure 7 represents $- (\partial n/\partial l)_\mu$ as a function of μ. It is seen to have a maximum at a concentration determined by the values of K_α and K_β, and it vanishes at the extreme concentrations $c = 0$ and $c = \sim$. The non-vanishing of $- (\partial n/\partial l)_\mu$ is a necessary though not sufficient condition for mechanochemical feasibility. Moreover, a large value of $- (\partial n/\partial l)_\mu$ is a favourable mechanochemical condition provided it is accompanied by a similar behaviour in the isophoric change, i.e. by a large value of $(\partial \mu/\partial l)_n$.

5.2.2. As a second criterium let us take the isopotential "mechanical capacity"

$$\left(\frac{\partial l}{\partial f}\right)_\mu = \frac{N_0}{AB \cdot RT}\,(l_{max} - l)(l - l_{min}) \qquad (d)$$

which represents a purely mechanical property of the autone model being dependent on l and independent of μ thus serving as a complementary measure to the first criterium, $(\partial n/\partial l)_\mu$, which depends on the chemical potential alone. Here again, the vanishing of $(\partial l/\partial f)_\mu$ indicates the impossibility of mechanochemical performance, since a rigid system cannot perform work. Moreover, $(\partial l/\partial f)_\mu = 0$ implies also $(\partial l/\partial f)_n = 0$ since it follows from eq. (32) that

$$0 \leqslant (\partial l/\partial f)_n \leqslant (\partial l/\partial f)_\mu \qquad (e)$$

A large value of $(\partial l/\partial f)_\mu$ is favourable for mechanochemical performance, provided it is accompanied by a small value of $(\partial l/\partial f)_n$, as may be readily inferred from the discussion in Section 4.2.3.

Since the maximum value of $(\partial l/\partial f)_\mu$ is at $l = -\frac{1}{2}(l_{max} + l_{min})$ irrespective of μ, while the maximum value of $-(\partial n/\partial l)_\mu$ is at $c = (K_\alpha K_\beta)^{-\frac{1}{2}}$ irrespective of l, it might be presumed that these two values determine the region of highest mechanochemical feasibility.

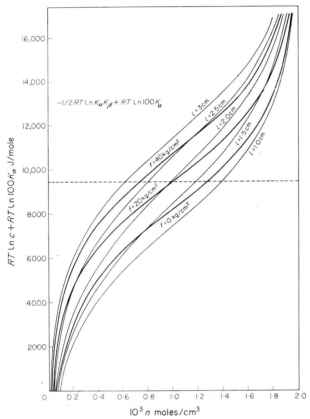

FIG. 6. Isotones (heavy lines) and isometrics (thin lines) for the autone model in the μ–n plane.

The ordinate represents the chemical potential on a shifted scale,

$$\mu + \text{const.} = RT \ln c + RT \ln 100 \, K_\alpha$$

It should be pointed out, however, that mechanochemical feasibility is not itself a uniquely determined single quantity, since we need a third criterium to complete the mechanochemical specification of the model. In fact one might add an arbitrary function of μ to

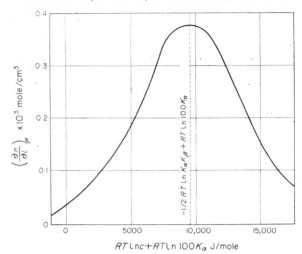

FIG. 7. The isopotential coupling coefficient $-(\partial n/\partial l)_\mu$ versus μ + const. for the autone model. The coefficient assumes it maximum value at $\ln c = -\frac{1}{2}\ln K_\alpha K_\beta$.

either eq. (a) or eq. (b) without changing the behaviour of the above chosen first two measures, although the mechanochemical features of the model might be in general altered considerably by the introduction of such changes.

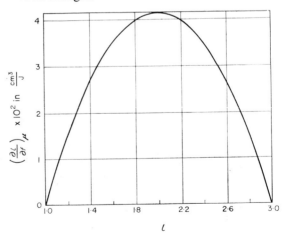

FIG. 8. Isopotential mechanical capacity $(\partial l/\partial f)_\mu$ of the autone model versus the length l of the engine.

5.2.3. As a third measure we might now introduce the iso-phoric–isopotential efficacy ϵ. Expressed as a function of l and μ it may be written as

$$\epsilon = (x\,AB/N_0RT)(b-a)^2\,[a(1-a)(l-l_{min})$$
$$+ b(1-b)(l_{max}-l)]^{-1} \qquad (f)$$

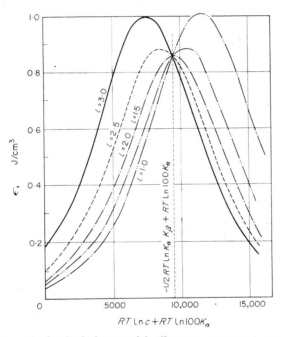

FIG. 9. The isophoric–isopotential efficacy ε versus μ + const. at different lengths l for the autone model. All the curves intersect at

$$\ln c = -\tfrac{1}{2}\ln K_\alpha\,K_\beta.$$

Figure 9 represents ϵ versus μ at different values of l. It is easily verified that the point of intersection of the various curves cor-responds to $c = (K_\alpha K_\beta)^{-\frac{1}{2}}$. However, it is only for the curve with $l = \tfrac{1}{2}\,(l_{max} + l_{min})$ that this point has a maximum efficacy. For other values of l the maximum efficacy is shifted and reaches higher values. On the other hand the efficacy alone is not only insufficient but even misleading as a mechanochemical criterium. This is evident from the fact that it obtains relatively high positive values for

$l = l_{max}$ and $l = l_{min}$. In these extreme cases both the isophoric and isopotential mechanical capacities tend to zero (eq. (e)), yet ϵ which is the difference between their reciprocal values, i.e. between the Young's moduli, tends to a finite positive limit.

5.2.4. Finally, we might consider the *mechanochemical ratio* as an alternative criterium. It has a definite advantage over the efficacy for the autone model since it tends to zero at $l = l_{max}$ and $l = l_{min}$

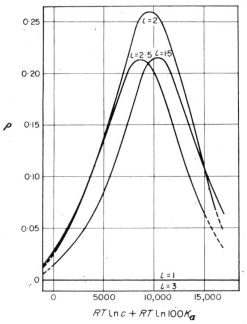

FIG. 10. The mechanochemical ratio ρ versus μ + const. at different lengths l for the autone model. Its highest maximum is at

$$l = \tfrac{1}{2}(l_{max} + l_{min}) \text{ and } \ln c = -\tfrac{1}{2} kn\, K_\alpha K_\beta.$$

for all values of ρ, as well as at $c = 0$ and $c = \sim$ for all values of l, i.e. in all the limiting cases of mechanochemically unfavourable conditions. Figure 10 represents ρ as a function of μ for some values of l. It obtains its maximal value at $l = -\tfrac{1}{2}(l_{min} + l_{max}, c = (K_\alpha K_\beta)^{-\frac{1}{2}}$, i.e. where $(\partial l/\partial f)_\mu$ and $(\partial n/\partial l)_\mu$ obtain also their maximal values as functions of l and c respectively. The region around $\rho = \rho_{max}$ may be considered therefore as the region of optimal mechanochemical performance.

REFERENCES

1. A. F. Huxley, *Progress in Biophysics and Biophysical Chem.*, vol. 7, p. 255 (ed. by J. A. V. Butler and B. Katz), Pergamon Press, 1957.
   H. H. Weber, *Ann. Rev. Biochem.*, vol. 36, p. 667 (ed. by J. Murray Luck), Annual Reviews Inc., 1957.
   E. Helander, *Acta Physiol. Scand.* **41**, suppl. 141 (1957).
   W. F. H. M. Mommaerts, *Methods in Med. Res.*, vol. 7, p. 1, Year Book Publ., 1958.
2. W. Kuhn, *Experientia* **5**, 318 (1949); A. Katchalsky, *ibid.* **5**, 319 (1949).
   W. Kuhn, B. Hargitay, A. Katchalsky and H. Eisenberg, *Nature* **165**, 515 (1950).
   J. W. Breitenbach and H. Karlinger, *Monatsh.* **80**, 211 (1949).
   K. H. Meyer, *Experientia* **7**, 361 (1951).
   A. Katchalsky and M. Zwick, *J. Polymer Sci.* **16**, 221 (1955).
   S. Basu and P. R. Chandhurry, *J. Colloid Sci.* **12**, 19 (1957).
   H. Yuki, Sh. Sakakibara, T. Taki and W. Tani, *Bull. Chem. Soc. Japan* **29**, 664 (1956).
3. J. Riseman and J. G. Kirkwood, *J. Am. Chem. Soc.* **70**, 2820 (1948).
   M. Morales and J. Botts, *Archiv. Biochem. Biophys.* **37**, 283 (1952).
   M. J. Polissar, *Am. J. Physiol.* **168**, 766, 782, 793, 805 (1952).
   M. G. M. Pryor, *Progress in Biophysics and Biophysical Chemistry*, vol. 1, p. 216 (ed. by J. A. V. Butler and J. T. Randall), Pergamon Press, 1950.
   D. R. Wilkie, *ibid.*, vol. 4, p. 288, 1954.
   A. F. Huxley, cf. ref. 1.
   M. F. Morales, J. Botts, J. J. Blum and T. L. Hill, *Physiol. Rev.* **35**, 475 (1955).
   I. M. Klotz and M. G. Horowitz, *Science* **126**, 3262 (1957).
4. A. V. Hill, *Proc. Roy. Soc.* B **139**, 464 (1952).
5. J. W. Gibbs, *Collected Works*, vol. I *Thermodynamics*, p. 184–218, Longmans Green, New York, 1931.
6. J. Rice, *A Commentary on the Scientific Writings of J. W. Gibbs* (ed. by F. G. Dennand and A. Haas), vol. I, p. 395 (1936).
7. W. W. Barkas, *Swelling Stresses in Gels*, Her Majesty's Stationery Office, London, 1945; *Trans. Faraday Soc.* **38**, 194 (1942).
8. F. L. Warburton, *Proc. Phys. Soc.* (*London*) **58**, 589 (1946).
9. G. Gurney, *Proc. Phys. Soc.* (*London*) **59**, 629 (1947).
10. G. Gee, *Trans. Faraday Soc.* **42**, 585 (1946).
11. L. R. G. Treloar, *Proc. Roy. Soc.* (*London*) A **200**, 176 (1950).
12. J. J. Hermans, *Proc. Intern. Congress Rheology, Holland, Amsterdam*, p. 117, North Holland Publ. Co., 1948.
    cf. also J. J. Hermans, *Flow Properties of Disperse Systems*, Cap. III, Gels, p. 61, North Holland Publ. Co., 1953.
13. T. L. Hill, *J. Chem. Phys.* **18**, 791 (1950).
14. H. J. White, *J. Chem. Phys.* **23**, 1491 (1954).
15. A. Katchalsky, *J. Polymer. Sci.* **7**, 393 (1951).
16. W. Kuhn and B. Hargitay, *Experientia* **7**, 1 (1951).
17. M. F. Morales and J. Botts, *Archiv. Biochem. Biophys.* **37**, 283 (1952).
18. T. L. Hill and M. F. Morales, *Archiv. Biochem. Biophys.* **37**, 425 (1952).
19. J. Gergely and K. Laki, *Enzymologia* **15**, 272 (1950).
20. T. L. Hill, *J. Chem. Phys.* **20**, 783 (1952).

21. M. J. POLISSAR, *The Kinetic Basis of Molecular Biology*, p. 699 (ed. by F. H. JOHNSON, H. EYRING and M. J. POLISSAR), John Wiley, New York, 1959.
22. W. KUHN, A. RAMEL, D. H. WALTERS, *Congress für Biochemie, Wien*, 1 September, 1958.
23. P. J. FLORY, *Science* **124**, 53 (1956).

CONVERSION OF CHEMICAL INTO MECHANICAL ENERGY BY HOMOGENEOUS AND CROSS-STRIATED POLYMERIC SYSTEMS*

by W. Kuhn, A. Ramel, and D. H. Walters

Institute of Physical Chemistry, University of Basel, Switzerland

SUMMARY

Conversion of chemical into mechanical energy is possible with the help of three-dimensional networks consisting of crosslinked macromolecules. The dilations and contractions of these systems are related to chemically produced changes of shape of non-crosslinked dissolved macromolecules.

In the first type of contractile system the dilations and contractions are produced by a change of ionization of the macromolecules making up the three-dimensional network. In a second type the dilations and contractions are due to a change in the state of oxidation of the network molecules ("redox-muscle"). In the latter system the energy of redox-processes is directly converted into mechanical energy by filament contraction.

A polymer system has been prepared furthermore in which the length changes of the filaments occur without alteration of the diameter. It consists of an alternating sequence of contractile and non-contractile layers. In the first example of this new type of filament, called "cross striated pH muscle", the contractions and dilations are caused by a pH-change in the outside solution.

This cross-striated pH system permits a detailed investigation of the conversion of chemical into mechanical energy. A study of the Donnan-equilibrium between the gel and the outside solution shows that stretching at constant cross-section of the contractile layer is associated with an increase, and contraction with a decrease of the H^+-ion concentration of the outside solution. The influence of the composition of the outside solution on the increase of the hydrogen ion concentration, produced by stretching the filament is discussed. The following cases are considered: the outside solution contains (a) a small amount of neutral salt; (b) no neutral salt; (c) buffer. The theoretical predictions for case (a) were confirmed by experiments.

As a result of these considerations and experiments it is proved that the free chemical energy corresponding to a chemically-induced stretching of the cross-

* Submitted July, 1958

striated system is equal to the mechanical energy associated with the contraction.

The description of conversion of chemical into mechanical energy with the help of a contractile polymer system has thus reached the same degree of precision as that of the production of mechanical from chemical energy by expansion and compression of gases (van't Hoff), or the production of electrical energy with Galvanic cells (Nernst).

1. CHANGE OF SHAPE OF MACROMOLECULES IN SOLUTION AND TRANSFER OF THIS CHANGE TO A MACROSCOPIC SCALE

Applying the results of earlier investigations on the form of macromolecules, a reversible change by chemical means of the shape of linear macromolecules in solution was intentionally produced for the first time some years ago.[1, 2] This was accomplished with a solution of polyacrylic acid in water; the addition of alkali and acid produced a stretching and contraction of the coiled molecules, disclosing itself by increase and decrease of the viscosity of the solution. The changes could be treated quantitatively.[3, 4]

Some time later, it was possible to transfer these changes of form from the microscopic scale realized in solutions to a macroscopic level. The individual filament molecules were, for this purpose, cross-linked together to form a three-dimensional network.[5, 6]

2. HIGH POLYMER FILAMENTS DILATING AND CONTRACTING OWING TO A CHANGE OF IONIZATION; THE "pH-MUSCLE" SYSTEM

An especially simple and effective system[5, 7-9] of this kind consisting, in the dry state, of 30–50% polyacrylic acid (PAA, formula I) and 70–50% polyvinyl alcohol (PVA, formula II) is obtained as follows: an aqueous solution containing equal quantities of PAA and PVA is allowed to dry on a glass plate; strips cut from foils thus obtained are heated for 30 to 40 min to 110°–120° without a load, or for 30 sec under a load of 50 to 100 kg cm^{-2}. The foils, which before this treatment were soluble in water, swell in water but are no longer soluble. They exhibit a strong reversible dilation and contraction owing to a change of pH of the surrounding liquid: dilation on addition of alkali, and contraction on addition of acid.

I

—CH$_2$ · CH · CH$_2$ · CH · CH$_2$ · CH · CH$_2$ · CH—
      | | | |
   COOH   COOH   COOH   COOH

Polyacrylic Acid

II

—CH$_2$ · CH · CH$_2$ · CH · CH$_2$ · CH · CH$_2$ · CH—
      | | | |
    OH   OH   OH   OH

Polyvinyl Alcohol.

When unloaded strips are chemically stretched by addition of alkali to the embedding-fluid and then made to contract by the addition of acid, with a weight attached to the lower end of the filament, mechanical energy is produced when the weight is lifted. The process of chemically stretching and making the filament lift a weight in the subsequent contraction can be repeated many times. In an experiment of long duration[19] in which a periodic change of pH (0·01 N HCl and 0·01 N NaOH) was produced, more than 1,750[19] contractions and dilations of the same strip were obtained, without the appearance of fatigue. The strip which had a dry weight of 50 mg and a length of 30 cm in the acid solution, was loaded with a weight of 2 g, and the lifting of this weight 1,750 times over a distance of 20 cm represented a work output of 0·7 mkg. As no other means than the addition of alkali and acid were used, it is obvious that the energy necessary for lifting the weight has been taken from the energy of the chemical reaction of the acid with the alkali employed. Chemical energy has by this contractile system, at least partly, been transformed into mechanical energy.[9]

It is known that the natural muscle is doing a similar thing: mechanical energy is, likewise, produced by contraction of a filament. If it is permissible to designate, generally, as a muscle a system[9] which is able to transform chemical energy into mechanical energy through contraction of a filament, the PAA-PVA-system described can be called a muscle or more exactly a "pH-muscle" because the dilations and contractions are produced by a pH change.

It is interesting to note that the analogy between the PAA–PVA-system and the natural muscle, besides the qualitative statement of a transformation of chemical into mechanical energy, encompasses a part of the quantitative properties such as tensile strength, value of the maximum contractile force, and the work done in calories per contraction per gram of contractile substance. This analogy is evident from Table 1.[9]

TABLE 1. COMPARISON OF NATURAL MUSCLE WITH FILAMENTS CONTAINING 80% POLYVINYL ALCOHOL AND 20% POLYACRYLIC ACID.

	Natural muscle	Artificial filaments (swollen in water)
Tensile strength (kg/cm²)	4–12	4–12
Contractile force (kg/cm²)	4–12	3– 5
Work in calories per contraction done per gram of contractile substance	15–20×10^{-2}	$7 \cdot 10^{-2}$
Force (maximum), divided by Weight of contractile substance in each cm of filament	15–60×10^{3}	15–$70 \cdot 10^{3}$

The dilation of the PAA–PVA-system caused by the alkali is due to the dilution tendency of the relatively concentrated Na-ion solution which is formed in the interior of the gel[9–11] owing to addition of alkali. The osmotic pressure, due to the sodium ions formed on complete neutralization of the PAA in a sample of the PAA–PVA gel, swollen in pure or slightly acid water, would be of the order of 100 atmospheres if the neutralization were carried out at constant volume of the gel. The limitation of the swelling occurring in the alkaline outside solution is determined both by the dilution of the sodium ion solution contained in the gel and by the stretching (and dilution) of the network filaments produced by the swelling.[9–11] The free energy corresponding to the stretching of the network filaments is understandable on the basis of the kinetic theory of rubber elasticity[12, 13] according to which each individual network filament of molecular weight M_f can be assigned an entropy depending on M_f, the length of the statistical chain element and on the magnitude of the vector h which connects the endpoints of the filament.

At equilibrium, the free energy change of the network, corresponding to additional swelling, will be equal to the osmotic work of the ionic solution in the gel. The magnitude of the restoring force on the addition of HCl to the NaOH-stretched system is understandable from the tendency of the filaments of the network to return from the improbable stretched state to the more probable conformation of a statistical coil.[12-14]

A direct proof for the indicated rôle of the PAA is given by the observation that foils consisting of pure PVA, otherwise prepared and treated in a similar way as the PAA–PVA strips described above, have the property to swell to a limited extent in water, without however showing any change in length after addition of alkali or acid.

3. FILAMENTS DILATING AND CONTRACTING OWING TO A CHANGE IN THE STATE OF OXIDATION; THE "REDOX-MUSCLE" AND THE "CHANGE-OF-SOLUBILITY-MUSCLE"

The comparison of the natural muscle with the PAA–PVA-system is impaired by the difference between the chemical energy which is converted into mechanical energy in the two systems. While the PAA–PVA-system obtains the energy from the neutralization of NaOH by HCl, the natural muscle obtains the energy essentially from the oxidation of glucose.

It is therefore of interest that it has recently been possible to produce a contractile system in which the contraction and dilation are brought about by chemical reduction and oxidation without any changes in the state of ionization of the macromolecule.[15, 16, 18]

The new system makes use of a copolymer prepared from vinyl alcohol and allylalloxan, the formula being indicated below, (I).[15, 16, 18] This copolymer is obtained by copolymerizing vinyl-acetate with n-allylbarbituric acid (reaction A), by oxidizing the barbituric acid to alloxan (reaction B) and, finally, by alcoholysis of the vinylacetate groups to vinyl alcohol (reaction C).

The copolymerization of vinylacetate with n-allylbarbituric acid (reaction A) is a radical polymerization, which proceeds in absence of air, in tetrahydrofuran or acetic acid solution. The catalyst was benzoylperoxide. The copolymer contained about 20 mol% of allylbarbituric acid. The oxidation of the allylbarbituric acid to alloxan (reaction B) occurred with chromium trioxide in acetic acid and the transformation of the acetate in alcohol (reaction C) by alcoholysis of the acetate groups with magnesium methylate in absolute methanol, a small quantity of sodium methylate being added as catalyst.

Preparation of the copolymer from vinyl alcohol and allyl-alloxan (see text)

A cross-linked foil composed of equal parts of this new copolymer and PVA was produced in a similar way as described above.[15] Strips of this foil swell in water to a limited extent, without being soluble. A pH change as a basis for contraction and dilation was excluded by using a $0 \cdot 1$ N acetate buffer solution. The alloxan in these strips can be reduced to dialuric acid with hydrogen and the latter can be oxidized to alloxan with oxygen. The alloxan and dialuric acid groups formed in the oxidation and reduction processes, are a redox system; these groups are fixed to the gel structure in the interior of the strip. The normal potential of this redox system has a value of approximately $E = 0 \cdot 3693$ volt, i.e. about the value which is characteristic for the redox system in water of free alloxan/free dialuric acid.

The reduction of an aqueous solution of alloxan to dialuric acid with hydrogen at room temperature and pH ~ 5 requires platinum as a catalyst. The alloxan in the copolymer cannot leave the gel and therefore cannot react with the platinum catalyst suspended in the outside solution. The redox action produced in the outer fluid by gaseous hydrogen and oxygen had therefore to be transferred to the alloxan and dialuric acid groups within the gel with a soluble redox system namely with 2-methylnaphthoquinone (III) and 2-methylnaphthohydroquinone (IV) (vitamin K component). The normal potential ($0 \cdot 394$ volt) nearly agrees with the normal potential of the alloxan-dialuric-acid system. The added soluble redox-system is therefore capable of transferring the redox action to the fixed system in the interior of the gel. The reversible redox chain represents the transfer of the redox action within the solution and from the solution into the gel[15–18] (p. 48).

The strips now show a completely reversible change in length: on reduction, a shortening of the original length of about 20%; on oxidation a dilation to the original value.

The reason for the contraction and dilation can be explained by the difference of solubility of alloxan, and the sodium salt of the dialuric acid. It is found that alloxan is easily soluble in water, that the sodium salt of the dialuric acid is sparingly soluble, and that the solubility characteristics of these groups have been carried over into the copolymers I and II. The latter phenomenon manifests itself in the case of the non-crosslinked dissolved copolymer in the precipitation of insoluble copolymer II if copolymer I is reduced. The precipitation of the non-crosslinked copolymer II corresponds to the contraction of the strips, made from the crosslinked copolymer. The emphasis on the cause of the contraction and dilation can be placed on oxidation and reduction, or on a chemically influenced change of the solubility of the gel constituents:[20b, 20c] (1) The free chemical energy arising from an oxidation and reduction process can be converted directly into mechanical energy in suitable cases with the use of a high polymer system. (2) Every chemical change of a macromolecular substance, provided it produces a change of the

Reversible redox chain showing the transfer of the redox action within the solution and from the solution into the gel.

SOLUTION

GEL

solubility of the polymer substance, can be employed for the production of mechanical energy from chemical energy. It can furthermore be stated that in such cases the free energy corresponding to the precipitation of an insoluble substance is utilized for the production of mechanical energy.

4. THE PREPARATION OF A CROSS-STRIATED HIGH POLYMERIC SYSTEM WITH ALTERNATING LAYERS OF DIFFERENT COMPOSITION[16-18]

There is a general swelling of the strips of both the PVA + Polyallyldialuric acid–alloxan system and the PVA + PAA system on oxidation or addition of alkali to the outside solution; the length, width, and thickness of the strip increasing by the same factor. A doubling of the original length during swelling corresponds to an increase of the volume by a factor of 8. On contraction, there is a general diminution in size of these strips.

The increase in volume by a factor of 8 impairs the analogy of this artificial system with the natural muscle. Therefore, it is of interest that it is possible by simple means to obtain a pH-sensitive system, i.e. filaments or strips which maintain a constant cross-section during the length changes brought about by reaction with alkali and acid.

Two different foils of approximately 0·1 mm thickness are produced by pouring the corresponding solutions on glass plates and allowing them to evaporate to dryness. The first foil (layer A of Fig. 1) consists of PVA. In order to differentiate it from the other foil (PVA + PAA) it was coloured black, a few drops of Indian Ink being added to the solution before it was poured over the glass plate. This foil was internally cross-linked by heating it for 120 minutes at 120°. There was only a moderate swelling of this foil in water, the water absorption being 50–100% of the dry weight. The second foil (layer B of Fig. 1) was obtained by evaporating an aqueous solution containing about equal parts of PVA and PAA. After drying, these foils were weakly cross-linked, either at room temperature or by a short period of warming. The black foils (containing only PVA) and the white foils (containing both PVA + PAA) were alternately placed on top of each other, like pages of a book after having been cut into circular or quadratic shape. The sandwich so obtained was placed in an evacuated glass flask into which a stream of dilute aqueous PVA solution was admitted. Under light pressure the adjacent sections of the sandwich were pressed against each other so that on subsequent slow drying a thin sheet of PVA would be present as a bonding agent. The resultant block, consisting of alternate white and black foils, was heated to 120° under light pressure for 30 min. The previously cross-linked black foils were thus made more strongly cross-linked, while the white foils (including the small amount of PVA which formed the link between the black and white foils) became insoluble in water but retained its ability to swell.

5. ONE-DIMENSIONAL CONTRACTION AND DILATION OF THE CROSS-STRIATED SYSTEM

When the block is deposited in water the swelling of the black foils is not significant while that of the white foils is substantial. The highly swollen white foils adhere on the entire surface of both

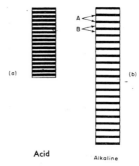

FIG. 1. Contractile and non-contractile layers of artificial cross-striated systems:

A Black layers: foils of pure PVA.
B White layers: foils containing equal parts of PVA and PAA.

        (a) = contracted state in acid solution.
        (b) = dilated state in alkaline solution.

sides to the slightly swollen practically rigid black foils. As a consequence of this, even during this first swelling in water, there is only an increase of length of the block* and no change of the lateral dimension.

* The word thickness as used throughout the remainder of the text refers to the height of the PAA-containing layer of the cross-striated system which dilates (relaxes) and contracts with a constant cross-section.

If the block is placed in a 10^{-2} N NaOH solution, the rigid black layers (containing only PVA) change very little while the white PAA-containing foils swell substantially as shown in Fig. 1. This swelling, however, increases only the thickness because the upper and lower surfaces of the white foils are fixed in their dimensions. On addition of acid the white foils de-swell to a degree characteristic of the equilibrium in pure water.

6. SPECIAL CHARACTERISTICS AND MODE OF OPERATION OF THE CROSS-STRIATED SYSTEM

The system [16-18] of white and black foils increases and decreases its thickness without a concomitant change in the lateral dimension, on addition of alkali or acid, these changes being reversible.

The change of the lateral dimension which occurs during dilation and contraction of the non-laminated system is avoided in the cross-striated system. Some absorption of solvent is admittedly necessary for lengthening of the cross-striated filaments, but the amount of fluid absorbed is much less than needed for a change in length in the case of three-dimensional swelling and de-swelling of a homogeneous filament. The increase in the cross-section and the solvent transport, associated with the three-dimensional swelling of the homogeneous filaments is useless for the conversion of chemical energy into mechanical energy; this is avoided in the case of the cross-striated system. The maintenance of the lateral dimension during chemically-induced swelling also prevents an excessive dilution of the gel substance and thereby maintains the tensile strength per cm² of the filaments; the cross-striated filaments are more advantageous, therefore, for the production of mechanical energy from chemical energy, than the homogeneous filaments.[17] The tearing force of the cross-striated filaments is about 15 kg/cm², in the experiments so far carried out.

It has been observed that the one-dimensional swelling produced by the alkali is accompanied by a strong optical birefringence owing to the anisotropic deformation of the contractile layers. Investigation with polarized light revealed the PAA-containing layers to be almost isotropic in an acid medium and to be highly birefringent in an alkaline medium as a result of the one-dimensional swelling.

An optical examination of the PVA and of the PAA layers was

possible if the PVA layers were not stained with Indian ink. This examination disclosed that the pure PVA layers which prevent the lateral swelling of the layers also show a certain birefringence. The tension which appears in the PVA layers is perpendicular to the tension which appears in the layer containing PAA; as a result a birefringence is observed in the two kinds of foils which are at right angles to each other.

In spite of the important differences in the behaviour of homogeneous and cross-striated systems the mode of operation is in its fundamentals nearly the same. Thus in the case of the "cross-striated pH-muscle" the dilation occurring on addition of alkali is essentially due to the dilution tendency of the sodium ion solution which has been produced in the interior of the gel.[9-11] The same state of affairs prevails in the case of the homogeneous "pH-muscle", the only difference being that the dilation is not uni-dimensional as in the case of the cross-striated system. There is a similar situation in the contraction produced by the addition of HCl to the alkali-dilated system, i.e. both the dilation and contraction can be explained qualitatively and quantitatively by the kinetic theory of rubber elasticity,[12, 13] and the Donnan theory of osmotic equilibrium, if properly applied to the prevailing conditions.

The optical birefringence observed in the case of the alkali-swollen cross-striated system can be explained by the treatment developed for the optical birefringence of stretched, swollen or bulk rubber.[12]

7. SOME ANALOGIES OF THE ARTIFICIAL CROSS-STRIATED SYSTEM WITH THE NATURAL CROSS-STRIATED MUSCLE*

The artificial cross-striated system embodies some of the functional and physical characteristics of the natural cross-striated muscle. There is biochemical evidence to show that the Z-membrane, which might be considered analogous to the black PVA layer, is a rigid, non-contracting structure.[21] Other data obtained by embryological[22, 23] histological electron microscope,[23-25] and chemical investigations support this hypothesis. The movement of water

* For further details concerning the comparison dealt with in this section see references 20b and 20c.

across the muscle membrane during contraction (de-swelling) and relaxation (swelling) is discussed elsewhere.[26] Birefringence studies[21, 27] of the natural cross-striated muscle have not been clarified for the specific areas, e.g. the A- and I-bands, except as regards the total birefringence of natural cross-striated muscle which decreases during contraction (de-swelling). The degree of analogy between the two systems is difficult to assess because the histochemical structure, the protein chemistry and the mode of action of the natural cross-striated muscle are not sufficiently investigated. There are several recent excellent reviews[27, 28] on the problems concerning the physiology and chemistry of skeletal muscle.

On the basis of our present knowledge[20b, 20c] one may assume that the Z-membrane of natural cross-striated muscle is a rigid, non-contracting structure which maintains a constant cross-section of the muscle myofibril during contraction (de-swelling) and relaxation (swelling), and thus prevents a three-dimensional swelling and permits only a one-dimensional swelling. This suggestion is applicable to the physiological range of shortening of the muscle and does not contradict any of the other possible functions of the Z-membrane.[29] It will now be shown that the artificial cross-striated pH-system is very useful for a quantitative investigation of the conversion of chemical energy into mechanical energy.[20] This aspect of the work is independent of any analogy between the fibres here considered and natural muscle.

8. EXISTENCE OF MECHANICAL AND CHEMICAL PATHWAYS FOR STRETCHING THE CONTRACTILE LAYERS OF THE CROSS-STRIATED SYSTEM

We consider, for this purpose, a contractile layer of cross-section a^2 of the cross-striated pH-system; this layer is placed between two rigid sheets of PVA, its cross-section being thus maintained constant throughout the following experiments. Partial neutralization of the PAA gives rise to a fraction a_1 of the COOH-groups being converted into the ionised sodium salt. The thickness of the layer, in equilibrium with a dilute aqueous medium, will have a definite value, say L_1. It is then possible, keeping a and the cross-section a^2 constant, to change L from L_1 to L_2 (Fig. 2) by mechanical stretching with an external force and it is possible, too, to get from the same initial state to the same final state by chemical means (path I and II of Fig. 2) involving pH changes of the outside solution.

We will calculate the free energies necessary for both ways and thereby demonstrate that they are in agreement with each other.

9. MECHANICAL INCREASE OF THE THICKNESS OF THE CONTRACTILE LAYER FROM L_1 TO L_2

When we increase the thickness of the contractile layer from L_1 to L_2 (under the conditions of a constant cross-section and constant

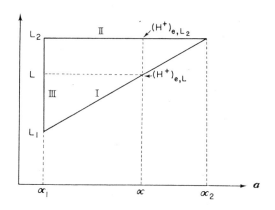

$$\frac{(H^+)_{e,L_2}}{(H^+)_{e,L}} = \frac{L_2}{L} \qquad (X^-) \simeq 10^{-1}$$
$$(NaCl) \simeq 10^{-3}$$

FIG. 2. Reversible conversion of chemical into mechanical energy. The height of the contractile layer L can be increased from L_1 to L_2, at a degree a_1 of ionization either directly along path III, or indirectly along paths I + II

degree of ionization), the force (K) per cm² which must be used to increase the thickness of the layer to the value L_2 is equal to

$$K = \frac{L_2 - L_1}{L_1} . E'. \tag{1}$$

The force necessary for a layer with the cross-section a^2 is equal to $K a^2$. E' is a kind of elasticity modulus; it is *not* the conventional

Young's Modulus of an elastic material, because in stretching [see equation (1)] the cross-section of the material is assumed to remain constant. The increase of thickness from L_1 to L_2, at constant cross-section, involves an increase of the volume of the layer from $v_1 = a^2 . L_1$ to

$$v_2 = a^2 . L_2 = v_1 . \frac{L_2}{L_1} = v_1 . \sigma. \tag{2}$$

For this increase (v_1 to v_2) in the volume of the gel (see also Fig. 3), a corresponding volume of water must enter the gel from the outside solution. It is clear that the stretching undertaken for the determination of E' according to equation (1) has to be much slower than in the determination of the conventional elasticity modulus; in the measurement of the latter no transfer of substance from the surroundings is presumed or permitted. Furthermore, E' in equation (1) is constant only as long as

$$\frac{L_2 - L_1}{L_1} \ll 1, \tag{3}$$

i.e., as long as the stretching is relatively weak. With a greater degree of stretching, E' would become a quantity dependent on $(L_2 - L_1)/L_1$. For simplicity we will accept the validity of equation (3) for what follows. The mechanical energy necessary for stretching the material from L_1 to L_2 at constant cross-section a^2 is then equal to

$$A = \int_{L_1}^{L_2} K(L) a^2 . dL = \tfrac{1}{2} E' . a^2 . L_1 \left(\frac{L_2 - L_1}{L_1}\right)^2. \tag{4}$$

10. CHANGE OF THE pH OF THE OUTSIDE SOLUTION PRODUCED BY A MECHANICAL CHANGE OF THE THICKNESS OF THE CONTRACTILE LAYER

In order to undertake the calculation of the chemical free energy necessary for the increase of the contractile layer via a chemical change, it is necessary to consider the change of pH of the outside solution corresponding to a mechanical change of the thickness of the contractile layer. For this purpose we will examine the Donnan-equilibrium, i.e. the distribution of the different kinds of ions between the contractile layer and the outside solution when the thickness of the contractile layer (which at a degree of ionization a_1, and in the absence of an external force is L_1), is increased by an external force at a constant cross-section from L_1 to L_2.

It will be seen that the pH change associated with the stretching from L_1 to L_2 is highly dependent on the presence in the outside solution of small quantities of a neutral salt such as NaCl or a buffer.

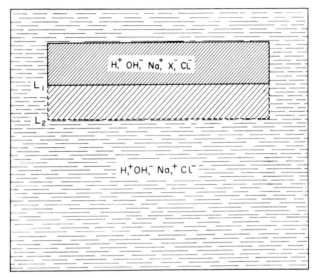

FIG. 3. Partition of ions as the result of a Donnan-equilibrium between the contractile layer (cross-hatched) and the outside solution. The ionic concentration of the outside solution is considered below under three different, specified conditions: 10a, 10b, and 10c.

(a) *pH change produced in an outside solution containing a small quantity of NaCl[20].*

We consider, in the first instance, the case in which the outside solution contains, besides the H^+ and OH^--ions, a small quantity of a neutral salt, say 10^{-3} moles of Cl^-- and Na^+-ions per litre. The concentrations of the Na^+, Cl^-, H^+, and OH^- ions in the outside solution, in Donnan-equilibrium with the gel layer of thickness L_1, will thus be $[Na^+]_{e, L_1}$, $[Cl^-]_{e, L_1}$, $[H^+]_{e, L_1}$, and $[OH^-]_{e, L_1}$ while the concentrations in the interior of the contractile layer are

$[Na^+]_{g, L_1}$, $[Cl^-]_{g, L_1}$, $[H^+]_{g, L_1}$, $[OH^-]_{g, L_1}$, and $[X^-]_{g, L_1}$, the latter designating the concentration of COO^- groups, due to the partial neutralization of the polyacrylic acid. If $[P]_{g, L_1}$ is the total concentration of polyacrylic acid (ionized and non-ionized) in the gel layer of thickness L_1:

$$[X^-]_{g, L_1} = a_1 [P]_{g, L_1} \qquad (5)$$

In the contractile layers used in our experiments, $[P]_g$ was approximately 0.5 to 1.0 g-equivalents of PAA per litre of the swollen gel. If a is equal to 0.1 to 0.5, we will according to equation (5) have $[X^-]_{g, L_1} = 0.05$ to 0.1 moles per litre. The total ion concentration in the gel will be much greater than in the outside solution if the chloride ion concentration in the outside solution is maintained at 10^{-3} moles per litre. It is known that in the Donnan-equilibrium the chloride ion concentration $[Cl^-]_{g, L_1}$ in the gel will then be negligible compared with $[Cl^-]_{e, L_1}$. (For further details concerning this statement and the following consideration leading to eq. (12) see reference 20b and 20c.) If the dissociation constant K_X of the polyacid in the gel is of the order of $K_X = 10^{-5}$ to 10^{-6}, $[H^+]_{g, L_1}$ and $[OH^-]_{g, L_1}$ will be small compared with $[Na^+]_{g, L_1}$ which therefore becomes

$$[Na^+]_{g, L_1} \simeq [X^-]_{g, L_1}, \qquad (6)$$

an equation from which we obtain,

$$[Na^+]_{g, L_1} = a_1 \cdot [P]_{g, L_1} \qquad (7)$$

if (5) is taken into account. As the hydrogen-ion concentration (or activity) in the gel is connected with K_X and the concentration of dissociated and undissociated polyacid, by the equation

$$[H^+]_{g, L_1} = K_X \frac{[HX]_{g, L_1}}{[X^-]_{g, L_1}} = K_X \frac{[P]_{g, L_1} \cdot (1 - a_1)}{[P]_{g, L_1} \cdot a_1}, \qquad (8)$$

we have

$$[H^+]_{g, L_1} = K_X \frac{1 - a_1}{a_1}. \qquad (8a)$$

If K_W is the ionization product of water we have furthermore:

$$[OH^-]_{g, L_1} = \frac{K_W}{K_X} \frac{a_1}{1 - a_1}. \qquad (9)$$

5

The H^+- and OH^--ion concentrations in the outside-solution then follows from the well known conditions

$$[H^+]_{e,\,L_1} \cdot [OH^-]_{e,\,L_1} = K_W, \tag{9a}$$

and

$$[Na^+]_{g,\,L_1} \cdot [OH^-]_{g,\,L_1} = [Na^+]_{e,\,L_1} \cdot [OH^-]_{e,\,L_1}. \tag{9b}$$

They give:

$$\left.\begin{aligned}[H^+]_{e,\,L_1} &= \frac{K_W}{[OH^-]_{e,\,L_1}} = \frac{K_W}{[Na^+]_{g,\,L_1}} \frac{[Na^+]_{e,\,L_1}}{[OH^-]_{g,\,L_1}} \\ &= \frac{[H^+]_{g,\,L_1} \cdot [Na^+]_{e,\,L_1}}{[Na^+]_{g,\,L_1}},\end{aligned}\right\} \tag{9c}$$

or, taking (8a) into account:

$$[H^+]_{e,\,L_1} = K_X \frac{1 - \alpha_1}{\alpha_1} \frac{[Na^+]_{e,\,L_1}}{[Na^+]_{g,\,L_1}}. \tag{9d}$$

An equation similar to (9) holds in the case that the thickness of the contractile layer has been increased by an external force from L_1 to L_2 (path III of Fig. 2). We have therefore:

$$[H^+]_{e,\,L_2} = K_X \frac{1 - \alpha_2}{\alpha_2} \frac{[Na^+]_{e,\,L_2}}{[Na^+]_{g,\,L_2}}. \tag{9e}$$

By this increase, the volume of the contractile layer has been increased by a factor:

$$\sigma = \frac{L_2}{L_1} \tag{10}$$

It is seen that this volume increase of the gel occurs by uptake of water from the outside-solution; chloride ions are practically absent inside the gel, if the length is L_1 or L_2; OH^--ions are present in small quantities outside and inside the gel. Sodium ions alone cannot be transported through the boundary of the gel in appreciable quantities because of the requirements of electroneutrality. Therefore, the increase of L from L_1 to L_2 dilutes the sodium ion concentration in the gel, the total concentration of PAA, and the concentration of ionized and of non-ionized polyacrylic acid each by the same factor σ. We have therefore

$$[Na^+]_{g,\,L_2} = \frac{1}{\sigma} [Na^+]_{g,\,L_1}, \tag{10a}$$

$$[P]_{g,\,L_2} = \frac{1}{\sigma}\,[P]_{g,\,L_1},\tag{10b}$$

and thus in analogy to (7)

$$a_2 = \frac{[Na^+]_{g,\,L_2}}{[P]_{g,\,L_2}} = \frac{\frac{1}{\sigma}\,[Na^+]_{g,\,L_1}}{\frac{1}{\sigma}\,[P]_{g,\,L_1}} = a_1,\tag{11}$$

i.e. the degree of ionization of the PAA, contained in the contractile layer is not changed by the mechanical stretching from L_1 to L_2. If α remains unchanged, we conclude from (8a) that the hydrogen-ion concentration in the gel remains unchanged too:

$$[H^+]_{g,\,L_2} = [H^+]_{g,\,L_1}.\tag{11a}$$

The same follows then for the $[OH^-]$-concentration:

$$[OH^-]_{g,\,L_2} = [OH^-]_{g,\,L_1}.\tag{11b}$$

For the hydrogen-ion concentration in the outside solution in Donnan-equilibrium with the stretched gel, we obtain from (9e), taking (11): into account

$$[H^+]_{e,\,L_2} = K_X\,\frac{1-a_1}{a_1}\,\frac{[Na^+]_{e,\,L_2}}{[Na^+]_{g,\,L_2}}\tag{11c}$$

Introducing (10a) and taking into account that

$$[Na^+]_{e,\,L_2} \simeq [Cl^-]_{e,\,L_2} = [Cl^-]_{e,\,L_1} = [Na^+]_{e,\,L_1}$$

according to the assumption that the NaCl concentration of the outside solution is maintained during the stretching of the gel layer we obtain with equation (9d)

$$[H^+]_{e,\,L_2} = [H^+]_{e,\,L_1} \cdot \sigma\tag{12}$$

i.e., stretching of the gel (at constant cross-section) from L_1 to L_2 which leaves the hydrogen-ion concentration inside the gel unaltered produces an increase of the hydrogen-ion concentration in the outside solution which is in equilibrium with the gel. This somewhat paradoxical situation is a consequence of equation (9b) characteristic for the Donnan-equilibrium: if the $[H^+]_{g,\,L}$ and $[OH^-]_{g,\,L}$-concentrations in the gel remain unaltered and if the Na^+-ion concentration in the gel is diminished by a factor σ, (eq. 10a), then the OH$^-$-concentration in the outside solution must decrease by a factor σ if the Na$^+$-ion concentration in the outside solution remains constant.

(b) *pH change produced in an outside solution containing no neutral salt*

A similar consideration gives a different result, (eq. 17) if the outside solution contains no neutral salt. If the assumption $0\cdot1 < \alpha_1 < 0\cdot5$ is maintained, eq. (7) will continue to be valid and we have again

$$[\text{Na}^+]_{g,\,L_1} = \alpha_1\,[\text{P}]_{g,\,L_1} \tag{13}$$

This is true in spite of the fact that a small amount of Na$^+$-ions will now appear in the outside solution and will be electrically neutralized by a practically equal amount of OH$^-$-ions. Thus

$$[\text{OH}^-]_{e,\,L_1} = [\text{Na}^+]_{e,\,L_1}, \tag{13a}$$

while

$$[\text{H}^+]_{e,\,L_1} = \frac{K_W}{[\text{OH}^-]_{e,\,L_1}} = \frac{K_W}{[\text{Na}^+]_{e,\,L_1}}. \tag{13b}$$

The amount of Na$^+$-ions leaving the gel will be so small that (13) will practically not be affected. For the same reason the stretching of the gel will leave α unchanged, thus

$$\alpha_2 = \alpha_1. \tag{13c}$$

Equation (8) will likewise hold for the interior of the gel.

Mechanical stretching from L_1 to L_2 will in the same way as described in section, (a) produce a dilution of the sodium ions in the gel, thus

$$[\text{Na}]^+{}_{g,\,L_2} = \frac{1}{\sigma}\,[\text{Na}^+]_{g,\,L_1}. \tag{14}$$

The [H$^+$]- and the [OH$^-$]-concentrations in the gel, corresponding to eq. (8), (8a), and (8b), remain unaffected; thus

$$[\text{H}^+]_{g,\,L_1} = [\text{H}^+]_{g,\,L_2} \tag{14a}$$

$$[\text{OH}^-]_{g,\,L_1} = [\text{OH}^-]_{g,\,L_2}. \tag{14b}$$

The ion concentration in the outside solution, after the stretching of the gel layer, will be analogous to (13a) and (13b):

$$[OH^-]_{e,\,L_2} = [Na^+]_{e,\,L_2} \tag{15a}$$

and

$$[H^+]_{e,\,L_2} = \frac{K_W}{[OH^-]_{e,\,L_2}} = \frac{K_W}{[Na^+]_{e,\,L_2}}. \tag{15b}$$

As far as the actual value of the H^+-ion concentrations in the outside solution before and after stretching of the gel layer is concerned, we obtain for the sample being at length L_1 from (13a) and from (9b)

$$[Na^+]_{g,\,L_1} \cdot [OH^-]_{g,\,L_1} = [Na^+]_{e,\,L_1} \cdot [OH^-]_{e,\,L_1},$$

or

$$a_1 \cdot [P]_{g,\,L_1} \cdot \frac{K_W}{K_X} \frac{a_1}{1-a_1} = [OH^-]^2_{e,\,L_1} = \frac{K_W^2}{[H^+]^2_{e,\,L_1}}, \tag{16}$$

if (13) and (8b) are taken into account. From this it follows that

$$\left. \begin{aligned} [H^+]_{e,\,L_1} &= \frac{K_W \cdot K_X \cdot (1-a_1)}{a_1 \cdot [P]_{g,\,L_1}}; \\[2mm] [H^+]_{e,\,L_1} &= \sqrt{\frac{K_W \cdot K_X}{[P]_{g,\,L_1}}} \frac{\sqrt{1-a_1}}{a_1}. \end{aligned} \right\} \tag{16a}$$

For the outside solution in equilibrium with the stretched gel, we will have similarly

$$[H^+]_{e,\,L_2} = \sqrt{\frac{K_W \cdot K_X}{[P]_{g,\,L_2}}} \frac{\sqrt{1-a_1}}{a_1} \tag{16b}$$

if $a_2 = a_1$. Comparison of (16a) and (16b), taking (10b) into account, gives:

$$[H^+]_{e,\,L_2} = [H^+]_{e,\,L_1} \cdot \sqrt{\sigma}. \tag{17}$$

From (15b) we obtain further

$$\left. \begin{aligned} [OH^-]_{e,\,L_2} &= \frac{K_W}{[H^+]_{e,\,L_2}} = \frac{K_W}{[H^+]_{e,\,L_1}} \frac{[H^+]_{e,\,L_1}}{[H^+]_{e,\,L_2}} \\[2mm] &= [OH^-]_{e,\,L_1} \cdot \frac{1}{\sqrt{\sigma}}, \end{aligned} \right\} \tag{17a}$$

and because of (13a) and (15a)

$$[Na^+]_{e, L_2} = [Na^+]_{e, L_1} \cdot \frac{1}{\sqrt{\sigma}}. \qquad (17b)$$

It is seen that in the present case, where the outside solution does not contain any neutral salt, a mechanical stretching of the gel layer from L_1 to L_2 is also associated with a decrease of pH; the hydrogen-ion concentration is increased by a factor $\sqrt{\sigma}$ while it was increased by a factor σ, according to eq. (12), which applies to the case in which a small amount of sodium chloride is present in the outside solution.

The comparison of the two cases shows that the change of state is the same as far as the interior of the contractile layer is concerned. In both cases the sodium-ion concentration in the gel is decreased by a factor σ, while α and the hydrogen-ion concentration in the gel remain constant. In the case of a small but constant NaCl concentration in the outside solution the change in the interior of the gel produces an increase of $[H^+]_e$ by a factor σ; in the case of no NaCl in the outside solution the same change in the interior of the gel produces a decrease of $[Na^+]_e$ and an increase of $[H^+]_e$ in the outside solution, the factor being $1/\sqrt{\sigma}$ and $\sqrt{\sigma}$ respectively.

(c) pH change produced by stretching the contractile layer, the outside solution containing a small amount of buffer

A similar statement can be made in a third case in which the outside solution contains a small amount of a buffer, consisting of an undissociated acid SH of concentration $[SH]_{e, L_1}$ and its sodium salt of concentration $[S^-]_{e, L_1}$. We assume that $[SH]_{e, L_1}$ is kept constant (e.g., saturation-concentration of a sparingly soluble weak acid). If K_S is the dissociation constant of the acid SH, the hydrogen-ion concentration for $L = L_1$ will be

$$[H^+]_{e, L_1} = K_S \frac{[SH]_{e, L_1}}{[S^-]_{e, L_1}}. \qquad (18)$$

If

$$[H^+]_{e, L_1} \gg [OH^-]_{e, L_1} = \frac{K_W}{[H^+]_{e, L_1}}, \qquad (18a)$$

we will furthermore have

$$[Na^+]_{e, L_1} + [H^+]_{e, L_1} = [S^-]_{e, L_1}. \qquad (18b)$$

If $K_S \ll 1$ and $[SH]_{e, L_1}$ is not too small and $[H^+]_{e, L_1} \simeq K_S$, i.e. if the degree of dissociation of the buffer in the outside solution is somewhat near $\frac{1}{2}$, $[H^+]_{e, L_1}$ will be much smaller than $[S^-]_{e, L_1}$ and we will have approximately

$$[Na^+]_{e, L_1} \simeq [S^-]_{e, L_1} \tag{18c}$$

Similar relations will hold for $L = L_2$.

If the values of the ion concentrations in the outside solution are small compared with the sodium–ion concentration in the gel, $([Na^+]_{g, L_1}$ or $[Na^+]_{g, L_2})$, the ionic concentrations inside the contractile layer will be determined by α_1, and the thickness L of the layer, [compare cases (a) and (b)], thus

$$\left. \begin{aligned} [H^+]_{g, L_1} = [H^+]_{g, L_2} &= K_X \frac{1 - \alpha_1}{\alpha_1}; \\[2mm] [OH^-]_{g, L_2} = [OH^-]_{g, L_1} &= \frac{K_W}{K_X} \frac{\alpha_1}{1 - \alpha_1}; \\[2mm] [Na^+]_{g, L_2} &= [Na^+]_{g, L_1} \cdot \frac{1}{\sigma}. \end{aligned} \right\} \tag{18d}$$

For $L = L_1$, the H^+- and OH^--ion concentrations in the outside solution will be determined, according to (9b), by the expression

$$[Na^+]_{g, L_1} \cdot \frac{K_W}{[H^+]_{g, L_1}} = [Na^+]_{e, L_1} \cdot \frac{K_W}{[H^+]_{e, L_1}},$$

or

$$[H^+]_{e, L_1} = [Na^+]_{e, L_1} \cdot \frac{[H^+]_{g, L_1}}{[Na^+]_{g, L_1}}. \tag{19}$$

The right hand side of this equation is, according to (18), and considering (18c), approximately equal to

$$[Na^+]_{e, L_1} \cdot \frac{[H^+]_{g, L_1}}{[Na^+]_{g, L_1}} = K_S \frac{[SH]_{e, L_1}}{[Na^+]_{e, L_1}}, \tag{20}$$

or

$$[Na^+]_{e, L_1} = \sqrt{K_S \cdot [SH]_{e, L_1} \frac{[Na^+]_{g, L_1}}{[H^+]_{g, L_1}}}. \tag{20a}$$

Introducing (20a) into (19) gives

$$[H^+]_{e, L_1} = \sqrt{K_S [SH]_{e, L_1} \frac{[H^+]_{g, L_1}}{[Na^+]_{g, L_1}}}. \tag{20b}$$

The equations similar to (20a) and (20b), valid for the stretched gel, i.e. for $L = L_2$ are

$$[Na^+]_{e,\,L_2} = \sqrt{K_S\,[SH]_{e,\,L_2}\,\frac{[Na^+]_{g,\,L_2}}{[H^+]_{g,\,L_2}}} \qquad (20c)$$

and

$$[H^+]_{e,\,L_2} = \sqrt{K_S\,[SH]_{e,\,L_2}\,\frac{[H^+]_{g,\,L_2}}{[Na^+]_{g,\,L_2}}}. \qquad (20d)$$

Considering that $[SH]_{e,\,L_2} = [SH]_{e,\,L_1}$ (according to assumption) and taking (18c) into account, we have

$$[Na^+]_{e,\,L_2} = [Na^+]_{e,\,L_1} \cdot \frac{1}{\sqrt{\sigma}} \qquad (21)$$

$$[H^+]_{e,\,L_2} = [H^+]_{e,\,L_1} \cdot \sqrt{\sigma} \qquad (21a)$$

$$[OH^-]_{e,\,L_2} = [OH^-]_{e,\,L_1} \cdot \frac{1}{\sqrt{\sigma}} \qquad (21b)$$

Comparison of (21), (21a) and (21b) with (17), (17a) and (17b) shows that the buffered outside solution, under the specified conditions, behaves in a similar manner to the unbuffered, salt-free outside solution, as far as the influence of stretching of the gel on the concentrations of the ions in the outside solution is concerned. The individual ion concentrations, e.g. $[H^+]_{e,\,L_1}$ are nevertheless different (see eqs. 20b and 16a).

(d) General case of dilute outside solution

The above considerations can be generalized for the case of any dilute outside solution. If the total ion concentration of the outside solution is small compared with the ion concentration inside the partially neutralized gel, the ionic state, i.e. $[H^+]_g$ and α inside the gel will not be influenced by stretching the gel from L_1 to L_2 (Fig. 2 and Fig. 3); the main alteration of the ion concentration inside the gel, on stretching, is the decrease of the sodium ion concentration $[Na^+]_{g,\,L_1}$ to $[Na^+]_{g,\,L_2} = [Na^+]_{g,\,L_1} \cdot \frac{1}{\sigma}$. Under these conditions, the general statement can be made that

$$[Na^+]_{g,\,L_2} \cdot [OH^-]_{g,\,L_2} = [Na^+]_{g,\,L_1} \cdot [OH^-]_{g,\,L_1} \cdot \frac{1}{\sigma},$$

and therefore on the basis of equation (9b) and the corresponding equation valid for $L = L_2$

$$[Na^+]_{e,\,L_2} \cdot [OH^-]_{e,\,L_2} = [Na^+]_{g,\,L_2} \cdot [OH^-]_{g,\,L_2}$$

$$= [Na^+]_{g,\,L_1} \cdot [OH^-]_{g,\,L_1} \cdot \frac{1}{\sigma},$$

and

$$[Na^+]_{e,\,L_2} \cdot [OH^-]_{e,\,L_2} = [Na^+]_{e,\,L_1} \cdot [OH^-]_{e,\,L_1} \cdot \frac{1}{\sigma}. \qquad (22)$$

The concentration of $[Na^+]_e$ and that of $[OH^-]_e$ or of $[H^+]_e$ in the outside solution may each vary in a different and complicated way when the contractile layer is stretched; the variation of $[Na^+]_e$ will however be coupled with a simultaneous variation of $[OH^-]_e$ or of $[H^+]_e$ in such a way that (22) will be fulfilled. In the foregoing case (a) we had

$$[Na^+]_{e,\,L_2} = [Na^+]_{e,\,L_1} \frac{1}{\sigma} \text{ and } [OH^-]_{e,\,L_2} = [OH^-]_{e,\,L_1} \cdot \frac{1}{\sigma},$$

in case (b) and case (c), we had

$$[Na^+]_{e,\,L_2} = [Na^+]_{e,\,L_1} \frac{1}{\sigma^{\frac{1}{2}}} \text{ and } [OH^-]_{e,\,L_2} = [OH^-]_{e,\,L_1} \frac{1}{\sigma^{\frac{1}{2}}}.$$

In all these cases (22) is fulfilled.

11. EXPERIMENTAL DEMONSTRATION OF THE pH CHANGE OF THE OUTSIDE SOLUTION[20]

It has been possible to demonstrate, by direct measurements, the pH change of the outside solution as produced by mechanical stretching. These experiments were done to confirm eq. (12). The experimental conditions were those assumed in (a) of the preceding section.

A cross-striated system[16-18] as reviewed in section 4, was prepared in which the non-contractile layers consisted of strongly cross-linked PVA, and the contractile layers consisted of a less strongly cross-linked mixture of equal parts of PVA and PAA. Forked non-contractile "tendons" were prepared of pure polyvinyl alcohol strips which had been strongly cross-linked by 4 hours of vulcanization at 120°, and were attached to both ends of the cross-striated system with the help of PVA and subsequent vulcanization. The final cross-striated strips consisted of 100 non-contractile and contractile layers.

This system was placed in a glass vessel containing a NaOH solution, which neutralized 10% of the PAA in the contractile layers. The sealed vessel was shaken for 12 hours, when the pH of the original sodium hydroxide solution had decreased to 5·7. The system was then brought into equilibrium with a 10^{-3} N sodium chloride solution; the cross-striated system had a height of 4·2 cm and a cross-section of 0·15 cm². The thickness of the individual non-contractile layer was 0·012 cm, on the average, that of the contractile layer was 0·03 cm, on the average.

The pH of the outside solution, containing sodium chloride, 10^{-3} N and a small amount of quinhydrone was measured potentiometrically, while the solution was stirred by a stream of nitrogen, which had been bubbled through alkaline pyrogallol. The oxygen-free nitrogen entered the solution in which the cross-laminated system was suspended through a stainless steel capillary tube. The nitrogen left the vessel through a U-shaped escape valve filled with paraffine oil to prevent the re-diffusion of air. The measurements were carried out at 21° in a room from which daylight was excluded. Figure 4 further illustrates the apparatus with the artificial cross-striated muscle in position.

The establishment of the equilibrium value of the pH required one to several hours, the time depending primarily on the diffusion time in relation to the dimensions of the system. When equilibrium is reached the pH value remained constant for approximately 24

FIG. 4. Apparatus for measuring pH-changes produced by cross-striated polymer fibre: cross-striated polymer system in outside solution (A); vulcanized PVA "tendons" (B); metal clamp for holding "tendon" (C); ground metal joint for holding clamp and pyrex tube (D); nylon thread (E); pulley (F); weight (G); weight level-adjustor (H); capillary tube for nitrogen gas (K); platinum electrode (L); salt bridge (M); saturated calomel reference electrode (N); pH meter LSH 151 (O); Pyrex tube (P).

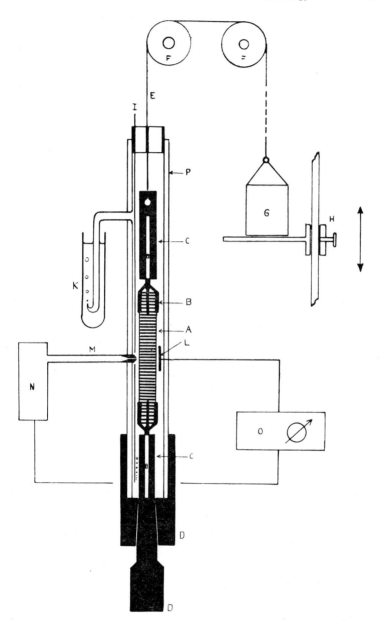

hours at one millivolt when the contractile system was unloaded. For the unloaded state an equilibrium pH value of 5·55 was obtained.

In 4 experiments, after obtaining the pH value characteristic for the unloaded system, a stretching of the cross-striated system was undertaken with a mechanical force of about 10 kg cm^{-2}. In order to do this, one end of the non-contractile "tendon" was held stationary at the bottom of the measuring cylinder and the other non-contractile "tendon" was attached by means of a non-elastic, chemically-inert nylon thread to a free-hanging weight (see Fig. 4). At first, as a consequence of the loading, a small sudden change in length occurred without a concomitant change in the pH of the outer fluid; this phenomenon was brought about by a rapid stretching at constant volume without the uptake of water and ions. With maintenance of the constant weight there was a subsequent uptake of water and a stretching of the PAA-containing layers of 190% of the original length. A stretching of the contractile layers by a factor of 1·9 gave rise to a potential increase of 14 mV, corresponding to a lowering of the pH of about 0·25 units; thus the H-ion concentration in the outside solution increased by a factor of 1·8 (average value). When the weight was removed the decrease of the H^{+}-ion concentration of the outside solution was proportional to the efflux of water and to the corresponding decrease of the thickness of the contractile layers.

Thus, the theoretically predicted pH shift of the outside solution, as a result of the stretching of the contractile layers held at constant cross-section, was observed within the accuracy of these first preliminary experiments.

12. FREE ENERGY FOR THE STRETCHING OF THE CONTRACTILE LAYER[20]

Returning to the problem of the transformation of chemical into mechanical energy we observe, as already mentioned in § 6, that a change in length of the contractile layer from L_1 to L_2 at constant cross-section and at a constant value of the degree of ionization a_1, as indicated in Fig. 2, can be undertaken either by mechanical stretching or by purely chemical methods: (1) the mechanically unloaded gel strip is dilated from L_1 to L_2 at constant cross-section by the addition of alkali (see path I of Fig. 2), i.e. by producing a suitable increase of the degree of ionization α, for example, from α_1 to α_2, and (2) the length is held constant at L_2 and the ionization degree is decreased from α_2 to α_1 (path II of Fig. 2). For the maintenance of a constant value of the length L_2 (as shown in the path II of Fig. 2) a mechanical device (but no mechanical work) is needed, to safeguard that in the transition I + II only chemical energy enters the system. This can be achieved through successive changes of the degree of ionization as mentioned above. If the dependence of the H^+- and Na^+-ion concentrations of the outside solution on the degree of the stretching of the contractile layers is taken into account it can be seen that the relevant ion concentrations to be used in corresponding steps of the transitions I and II are different.

The consideration will be carried through in detail first for a contractile layer suspended in a dilute (10^{-3} normal) NaCl solution (for which the experimental proof of a dependence of pH on stretching has been carried out). The corresponding consideration for a dilute outside solution of arbitrary composition will be given later.

(a) *Chemical change necessary for a given increase of the thickness L of the unloaded contractile layer*

In attempting to explain in detail the chemical operations needed for the chemical stretching of the contractile layer, it is of interest to determine the change $d\alpha$, of the degree of ionization of the contractile layer, necessary to increase the height L of the unloaded layer by an amount dL. For this purpose we consider an intermediate stage of path I, Fig. 2, the degree of ionization α lying somewhere between α_1 and α_2 and the height having a value $L > L_1$. The sodium ion concentration in the contractile layer is, according to equations (6) and (5)

$$[Na^+]_{g,\,L} = [X^-]_{g,\,L} = \alpha\,[P]_L = [\alpha_1 + (\alpha - \alpha_1)][P]_L. \qquad (23)$$

The force per cm² of the gel surface which is exerted by the Na^+-ions contained in the gel, i.e. the osmotic pressure of the Na^+-ion solution, is

$$RT \,.\, \alpha\,[P]_L = RT\,\alpha_1\,[P]_L + RT\,(\alpha - \alpha_1)[P]_L, \qquad (23a)$$

where R is the gas constant and T the absolute temperature. This force per cm² of the gel surface, the degree of ionization being a, exceeds by an amount $RT(a - a_1)[P]_L$ the force per cm² if the ionization degree is a_1, i.e. the increase of the degree of ionization from a_1 to a is equivalent to an expanding mechanical force. This force is given, per 1 cm², by

$$K = RT(a - a_1)[P]_L. \tag{23b}$$

Taking equation (1) into account it will be seen that

$$\frac{L - L_1}{L_1} = \frac{RT(a - a_1)[P]_L}{E'}. \tag{23c}$$

According to (10b) and (10) $[P]_L$ is given by

$$[P]_L = [P]_{L_1} \cdot \frac{L_1}{L} = [P]_{L_1} \frac{1}{1 + \dfrac{L - L_1}{L_1}}$$

In expanding the latter expression we neglect

$$\frac{L - L_1}{L_1} \text{ against 1 (see equation 3)}$$

and obtain $[P]_L \simeq [P]_{L_1}$. It follows, therefore, that

$$L - L_1 \simeq L_1 \frac{RT(a - a_1)[P]_{L_1}}{E'} \tag{23d}$$

which is but slightly different from (23c). In this approximation L is linearly associated with the value of the degree of dissociation a of the PAA present in the contractile gel layer (Fig. 2). There exists, according to equation (23d), a quantitative relationship between the change dL of the height of the gel layer and the corresponding degree of dissociation, da; this is

$$da = dL \frac{E'}{RT \cdot L_1 \cdot [P]_{L_1}}. \tag{23e}$$

This expression connects the chemical change da with a change dL and the elasticity modulus E' appropriate to a mechanical stretching at constant cross-section.

The change da requires the transformation of

$$dn = [P]_L \cdot a^2 \cdot L \, da = [P]_{L_1} \cdot a^2 \cdot L_1 \cdot da \tag{24}$$

moles of PAA inside the contractile layer from the non-ionized into the ionized state (a^2 is the cross-section of the contractile layer). In order to obtain this change, it is necessary to introduce into the outside solution dn moles of NaOH, the OH$^-$-ion concentration being

$$[OH^-]_{e,\,L} = \frac{K_W}{[H^+]_{e,\,L}},$$

and the Na$^+$-ion concentration being $[Na^+]_{e,\,L} = 10^{-3}$. Alternatively one can withdraw from the outside solution the amount of dn moles of HCl, the H$^+$-ion concentration being $[H^+]_{e,\,L}$, and the Cl$^-$-ion concentration being 10^{-3}M.

(b) *Chemical change necessary for a decrease* da *in the degree of ionization of the stretched layer kept at a constant thickness* L_2.

In a later phase, on passing over path II of Fig. 2, the ionization degree of the gel must be changed from $a + da$ to a; consequently, we will have to add dn moles of HCL (see equation 24) to the outside solution. On the occasion of the transition of path II the thickness of the contractile layer is equal to L_2 which exceeds the thickness relating the transition of a to $a + da$ in path I, by the factor $L_2/L = \sigma$.

(c) *Free chemical energy necessary for chemically stretching the unloaded layer from* L_1 *to* L_2 *and for bringing the degree of ionization of the layer of thickness* L_2 *back from* a_2 *to* a_1.

According to equation (12) the number of H$^+$-ions* to be added to the outside solution in path II exceeds the number of H$^+$-ions* which were withdrawn from the outside solution during the transition from a to $a + da$ in path I, Fig. 2 the factor being σ. This means that in order to increase the degree of ionization of the unloaded gel of length L from a to $a + da$, and later to reduce the degree of ionization of the loaded gel of length L_2 from $a + da$ to a dn moles of H$^+$-ions* equation (24) must be transferred, thereby changing the concentration $[H^+]_{e,\,L}$ to the concentration

$$[H^+]_{e,\,L_2} = \frac{L_2}{L}[H^+]_{e,\,L} = \sigma\,[H^+]_{e,\,L}$$

* Per unit volume.

The osmotic work required for this is

$$dA = dn \cdot RT \ln \sigma = [P]_{L_1} \cdot a^2 L_1 \, da \cdot RT \ln \frac{L_2}{L}. \tag{25}$$

The osmotic work A which is used for the transition corresponding to the complete paths I and II, is obtained when the expression (25) is integrated between the limits $a = a_1$ and a_2 thus

$$A = [P]_{L_1} \cdot a^2 \cdot L_1 \cdot RT \int_{a_1}^{a_2} \ln \frac{L_2}{L} \, da. \tag{25a}$$

We can see that in the case of $(L_2 - L)/L \ll 1$ we obtain

$$\ln \frac{L_2}{L} = \ln \left(1 + \frac{L_2 - L}{L} \right) \simeq \frac{L_2 - L}{L},$$

When the value for $\ln (L_2/L)$ is introduced in equation (25a), and equation (23e) for da is considered, we obtain the following expression for the osmotic work:

$$A = \int_{L_1}^{L_2} E' \cdot a^2 \frac{L_2 - L}{L} \, dL. \tag{25b}$$

Integration of (25b) gives

$$A = E' \cdot a^2 \cdot \left[L_2 \ln \frac{L_2}{L_1} - (L_2 - L_1) \right].$$

Representing the logarithmus as a series up to the quadratic members we arrive at

$$A = E' \cdot a^2 \left[L_1 \left(\frac{L_2 - L_1}{L_1} \right)^2 - L_1 \tfrac{1}{2} \left(\frac{L_2 - L_1}{L_1} \right)^2 \right.$$
$$\left. - \frac{L_1}{2} \left(\frac{L_2 - L_1}{L_1} \right)^3 + \ldots \right].$$

Neglecting the cubic member of this expression, equation (25b) becomes

$$A = \tfrac{1}{2} E' a^2 \cdot L_1 \left(\frac{L_2 - L_1}{L_1} \right)^2. \tag{25c}$$

Equation (25c) is identical with equation (4) and therefore the following statement may be made: the osmotic work which is necessary to increase, by removal and addition of HCl, the height of the gel layer equals exactly the mechanical work exerted during the contraction of the filament (when the chemically-stretched filament lifts a weight from L_2 to L_1).

As already mentioned, the withdrawal of dn moles of H^+-ions of the concentration $[H^+]_{e, L}$ from the outside solution is equivalent to the addition of dn moles of OH^--ions of the concentration

$$[OH^-]_{e, L} = K_W/[H^+]_{e, L},$$

Thus, when we increase the degree of ionization of the gel (path I of Fig. 2) by the addition of OH^--ions of the concentration $K_W/[H^+]_{e, L}$ (and Na^+-ions of the concentration 10^{-3} mol l^{-1}), and when we decrease the degree of ionization path II of Fig. 2) by the addition of H^+-ions of the concentration $[H^+]_{e, L} \cdot (L_2/L)$ (and Cl^--ions of the concentration 10^{-3} mol l^{-1}), then the free energy of neutralization of NaOH and HCl equals the mechanical energy produced by lifting the weight in the mechanical contraction (L_2 to L_1) of the chemically-stretched filament, i.e. with the aid of the polymer system the free energy of neutralization, that is to say the free energy of a chemical reaction is transformed quantitatively into mechanical energy.

(d) *Generalization*

The proof of a quantitative transformation of chemical into mechanical energy with the help of a cross-striated pH-muscle has been given above for the case that the dilute outside solution contains a neutral salt such as NaCl (e.g. 10^{-3} M). In this case, a stretching (at constant cross-section) of the contractile layer produced an increase of the hydrogen ion concentration in the outside solution which is directly proportional to the stretching, the factor being $\sigma = L_2/L_1$.

We have seen, however, that the increase of the hydrogen ion concentration on stretching is not necessarily proportional to σ; it may be proportional to $\sqrt{\sigma}$, as in case b and c of § 10. It is possible to show that also in this general case there is a quantitative conversion of chemical into mechanical energy, as long as the out-

6

side solution is dilute compared to the solution inside the gel. We apply for this the considerations of sections a, b, and c of this section to the general case of a dilute outside solution (cf. paragraph 11).

In order to produce an increase, dL, of the height of the unloaded contractile layer, an increase $d\alpha$, as defined by equation (23e) will be necessary also in the general case. If the sodium and hydroxyl ion concentrations in the outside solution in equilibrium with the contractile layer of thickness L, are $[Na^+]_{e,\ L}$ and $[OH^-]_{e,\ L}$, it will be necessary, in order to produce the increase $d\alpha$, to add to the outside solution dn equivalent OH^-- and Na^+-ions of the concentration just mentioned, dn being given by equation (24). In order to decrease the degree of ionization by $d\alpha$, corresponding to path II, Fig. 2, where the thickness of the contractile layer is L_2, dn equivalent Na^+-ions of the concentration $[Na^+]_{e,\ L_2}$ and the same amount of OH^--ions of the concentration $[OH^-]_{e,\ L_2}$ have to be withdrawn from the outside equilibrium-solution. The osmotic energy dA which is required to increase the degree of ionization of the unloaded contractile layer by $d\alpha$ and to decrease it again, when the layer has attained the length L_2, is therefore equal to the sum of the osmotic work for dn equivalent sodium and OH^--ions. This is given by

$$
\begin{aligned}
dA &= dn \ . \ RT \ln \frac{[Na^+]_{e,\ L}}{[Na^+]_{e,\ L_2}} + dn \ . \ RT \ln \frac{[OH^-]_{e,\ L}}{[OH^-]_{e,\ L_2}} \\
&= dn \ . \ RT \ln \frac{[Na^+]_{e,\ L} \ . \ [OH^-]_{e,\ L}}{[Na^+]_{e,\ L_2} \ . \ [OH^-]_{e,\ L_2}} .
\end{aligned}
\right\} \tag{26}
$$

This is, according to the general equation (22) equal to

$$dA = dn \ . \ RT \ln \sigma. \tag{27}$$

This is identical with equation (25). The integration of (27) is identical with (25a), (25b), giving the result (25c) which again is identical with equation (4).

It is thus proved that the osmotic work for chemically increasing the thickness of the contractile layer (path I + II of Fig. 2), from L_1 to L_2 is independent of the composition of the (dilute) outside solution. This is compatible with the fact that the dependence of the pH of the outside solution on the degree of stretching of the contractile layer is highly dependent on the composition of the outside solution.

The description of conversion of chemical into mechanical energy with the help of a contractile high polymeric system has thus[20] reached the same degree of precision, as that of production of mechanical from chemical energy through the expansion and compression of gases (van't Hoff), or that of conversion of electrical into chemical energy by means of galvanic cells (Nernst). In their paper[9] on homogenous gel filaments, W. Kuhn and B. Hargitay referred to the reversibility of the contractions and dilations and they postulated, thermodynamically, a quantitative conversion of chemical into mechanical energy. A detailed description of the energy conversion achieved with the help of the "cross-striated pH-muscle",[20] has now been given for the first time.

ADDENDUM

For a more detailed description of 1°, the cross-laminated pH-muscle; 2°, the homogeneous pH-muscle; 3°, the redox-muscle; 4°, the ion-precipitation-muscle and 5° the general and quantitative establishment of the teinochemical principle ($\tau \epsilon \acute{\iota} \nu \epsilon \iota \nu$ = to stretch, to dilate) see the following references: 1°, Ref. 20b, 20c, 30, 34; 2°. Ref. 31; 3°, Ref. 20b, 20c, 32; 4°, Ref. 20b, 34; 5°, 20b, 20c, 33, 34.

REFERENCES

1. W. KUHN, O. KÜNZLE, and A. KATCHALSKY, *Bull. Soc. Chim. Belgique* **57,** 421 (1948).
2. J. J. HERMANS and J. TH. G. OVERBECK, *Bull. Soc. Chim. Belgique* **57,** 154 (1948), and *Rec. Trav. chim. Pays-Bas* **67,** 761 (1948).
3. A. KATCHALSKY, O. KÜNZLE, and W. KUHN, *J. Polymer Sci.* **5,** 283 (1950).
4. O. KÜNZLE, *Rec. Trav. chim. Pays-Bas* **68,** 699 (1949).
5. W. KUHN, B. HARGITAY, A. KATCHALSKY, and H. EISENBERG, *Nature* **165,** 515 (1950).
6. W. KUHN, *Experientia*, **5,** 318 (1949); A. KATCHALSKY, *Experientia*, **5,** 319 (1949).
   J. W. BREITENBACH and H. KARLINGER, *Monatsh. Chem.* **80,** 311 (1949).
7. There are other systems of this kind in the literature, e.g.:
   A. KATCHALSKY, *Nature* **166,** 267 (1950); R. M. FUOSS and D. EDELSON, *J. Polymer Sci.* **6,** 523 (1951).
7a. F. G. E. PAUTARD and P. T. SPEAKMAN, *Nature* **185,** 176 (1960).
8. W. KUHN and B. HARGITAY, *Experientia* **7,** 1 (1951).

9. W. KUHN and B. HARGITAY, Z. Electrochem. angew. physik. Chem. **55**, 490 (1951). Lecture by W. KUHN at the 50th Annual Meeting of the Bunsen Society in Göttingen on 4 May 1951.

10. W. KUHN, Z. angew. Physik **4**, 108 (1952).

11. The recognition of the importance of the Donnan-osmotic force for this mechano-chemical system was first described and formulated quantitatively in reference 9. Later in the same year, it was re-discussed by A. KATCHALSKY (A. KATCHALSKY, S. LIFSON, and H. EISENBERG, J. Polymer Sci. **7**, 571 (1951)). For further discussions and development of this theory, see: P. J. FLORY, J. Chem. Phys. **21**, 162 (1953); T. L. HILL, Faraday Soc. Disc. No. 13 (1953), and Physiol. Rev. **35**, 475 (1955); S. ASAKURA, N. IMAI, and F. OOSAWA, J. Polymer Sci. **13**, 499 (1954).

12. W. KUHN. Koll. Z. **76**, 258 (1936), and W. KUHN, R. PASTERNAK, and H. KUHN, Helv. Chim. Acta **30**, 1705 (1947). This treatment was adopted and carried on by many authors, especially L. R. G. TRELOAR, Trans. Faraday Soc. **40**, 59 (1941), **39**, 36, 241 (1943); H. M. JAMES and E. GUTH, Ind. Eng. Chem. **33**, 624 (1941); H. M. JAMES, and E. GUTH, J. Chem. Phys. **11**, 455 (1943); **15**, 669 (1947); F. T. WALL, J. Chem. Phys. **10**, 485 (1942); **11**, 512 (1943); G. GEE, Trans. Faraday Soc. **42**, 585 (1946); H. M. JAMES and E. GUTH, J. Polymer Sci. **4**, 153 (1949).

13. W. KUHN and F. GRÜN, Koll. Z. **101**, 248 (1942).

14. The kinetic origin of the contractile force in the organism was first recognized by E. WÖHLISCH. Later, the importance of the form of the molecule was emphasized in particular by K. H. MEYER. See: E. WÖHLISCH, Verhandl. physik. Med. Ges. Würzburg, N.F. **51**, 53 (1926); K. H. MEYER, G. V. SUSICH and E. VALKO, Koll. Z. **59**, 208 (1932); K. H. MEYER and C. FERRI, Helv. Chim. acta **18**, 570 (1935).

15. A. RAMEL, Ph.D. Dissertation, Univ. of Basel (1957).

16. W. KUHN, Angew Chem. **70**, 58 (1958).

17. W. KUHN, A. RAMEL, and D. H. WALTERS, Chimia **12**, 123 (1958).

18. W. KUHN, A. RAMEL, and D. H. WALTERS, Angew. Chem. **70**, 314 (1958).

19. M. THÜRKAUF, Unpublished data (1957–1958). (Automatically controlled, continous performance of the "pH-muscle" carried out by Dr. M. Thürkauf during the International Exhibition, Palais de Science, Brussels, in June and July 1958, has shown that a foil is capable of 1,750 contractions and dilations.

20a. W. KUHN, A. RAMEL, and D. H. WALTERS, Nature **182**, 762 (1958); abstract from paper presented by W. KUHN at University College, London, 14 April 1958.

20b. W. KUHN, A. RAMEL, D. H. WALTERS, G. EBNER and H. T. KUHN, Fortschr. Hochpolym. Forsch. (Advances in Polymer Science) **1**, 541–592 (1960).

20c. W. KUHN, A. Ramel, and D. H. WALTERS, Proc. IV Intern. Congress Biochem., Vienna, 1958, Vol. 9, pp. 174–209. Pergamon Press, 1959.

20d. W. KUHN, A. RAMEL, and D. H. WALTERS, Bull. Soc. Industrielle de Mulhouse: (1) Resumés, (2) Communications des Journées Scientifiques de Mulhouse, 21–23 May 1958. (In press.)

20e. W. KUHN, Lecture at Sitzung der Math.-nat. Klasse, Dec. 8, 1957, Sitzungsberichte Heidelberger Akademie d. Wissenschaften Math. naturwiss. Kl. 1958, 545

21. N. NEURATH and K. BAILEY, The Proteins (Acad. Press), part B, vol. 2, p. 951, Academic Press, New York, 1954.

22. J. T. RANDALL, J. Cell. Comp. Physiol., Suppl. 1, **49**, 199 (1957).

23. H. E. JORDAN, *Am. J. Physiol.* **13**, 302 (1933).
24. A. H. DRAPER and A. HODGE, *Austral. J. Exper. Biol. and Med. Sci.* **27**, 465 (1949).
25. F. S. SJÖSTRAND and E. ANDERSSON-CEDERGREN, *J. Ultrastructure Research* **1**, 74 (1957).
26. E. BOLZER, *Arch. Biochem. and Biophysics* **73**, 144 (1958).
27. S. V. PERRY, *Physiol. Rev.* **36**, 2 (1956).
28. F. BUCHTHAL, *Physiol. Rev.* **36**, 503 (1956).
29. A. F. HUXLEY and R. E. TAYLOR, *Nature* **176**, 1068 (1955).
30. W. KUHN, *Chimia* **12**, 297 (1958); *Kunststoffe-Plastics* **5**, 347 (1958).
31. W. KUHN, G. EBNER, H. J. KUHN und D. H. WALTERS, *Helv. Chim. Acta.* **43**, 502 (1960).
32. W. KUHN, G. EBNER, H. J. KUHN und D. H. WALTERS, *Experientia* **16**, 106 (1960).
33. W. KUHN, D. H. WALTERS, H. J. KUHN und G. EBNER, *Z. Electrochem. angew. physik. Chem.* **64** (1960) in press.
34. W. KUHN, *Makromolekulare Chemie* **35**, 2. Sonderband, 200–221 (1960).

3

INDICATIONS ON MUSCLE CONTRACTION FROM X-RAY DIFFRACTION STUDIES OF THE FIBROUS PROTEINS

by W. T. Astbury, f.r.s.

Department of Biomolecular Structure, University of Leeds

Against the background of a wide range of X-ray diffraction and related studies muscle contraction appears not as something unique but rather as a special manifestation, fundamentally, of configurational changes associated with a whole family of fibrous proteins. The story begins with the first demonstration, in wool and other mammalian hairs, of polypeptide chains existing normally in a coiled or folded state from which they can be pulled out straight, only to coil up again when the tension is released.[1, 2] The unstretched form of the hair protein was called α-keratin and the stretched form β-keratin, and the two configurations, and the long-range elasticity deriving from their interchange, were thereafter shown to be common also to the principal muscle protein, myosin; the fibrous protein of the epidermis, epidermin; and the blood-clotting proteins, fibrinogen and fibrin. The group was then named the *k–m–e–f group*, but it has since been found to include besides the muscle proteins paramyosin and tropomyosin, and the structural protein of bacterial flagella, flagellin.[8] The α- and β-configurations, and the X-ray diagrams by which they are characterized, are now very familiar, though their detailed interpretation is still far from complete. It is generally agreed that the "α-helix" of Pauling and Corey[3] is the essential basis of the α-configuration and it has been unambiguously identified as such in certain synthetic polypeptides, but there are added features in the biological α-configuration that probably have to do with a second spiralization ("coiled coil").[4]

Not so familiar, though discovered almost as long ago as the α–β transformation, is the "supercontracted" state[2] which is also characteristic of members of the k–m–e–f group, and which seems so peculiarly related to muscle contraction[5] and on that account provides the main inspiration of this article. Omitting experimental procedures, on which sufficient has been published already, the central finding is that not only can the α-form be extended to the (about twice as long) β-form—and the transition has been demonstrated in preparations of muscle itself—it can moreover be caused to *shorten* ("supercontract", to distinguish from the contraction of the β-form back to the α-form) down to about half its original length. Nothing could have been more natural therefore, when the effect was found in myosin too,[6] than to propose that, shorn of all trimmings, here must be the fundamental molecular event in muscle contraction—and before proceeding farther, let it be emphasized again that there is no support, either from X-rays or from infra-red, for any suggestion that muscle contraction involves the $\beta-\alpha$ transition. The X-ray diagrams of relaxed muscle, living or dead, reveal only the α-configuration for the myosin component, thus, by the way, satisfying at least the requirement of a structure that can "give", whatever the mechanism of contraction may be. (The actin component, lying in parallel, is the source of the higher axial periodicities seen in X-ray diagrams of skeletal muscle.[7, 8])

We at Leeds have persevered for many years in this idea that muscle contraction is in the last resort only a manifestation of the supercontraction of myosin, but it was long before we could make any real headway beyond the corollary that the latter very likely came about by virtue of the α-configuration (in those days supposed to consist of a succession of square folds) falling into even longer folds transverse to the fibre axis, thus:

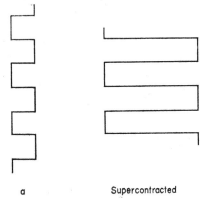

a   Supercontracted

About that time, though, came also the discovery of an anomalous
β-diagram in which the 4·65 Å reflection, which is a measure of
the CO ... NH separation of polypeptide chains and which appears
on the equator when fibres of the k–m–e–f group are simply *stretched*
into the β-form, was found instead on the meridian. This curious
phenomenon had actually been noticed first, in the early thirties,
after a frog sartorius muscle had been immersed (and thereby
rapidly contracted) in water at about 60°, but we did not understand it then, and it was somewhat later that we observed it again,
during the experiments with Bailey in which we showed that globular
proteins were three-dimensionally folded systems of polypeptide
chains which unfolded on denaturation and were afterwards capable
of being pulled out into "molecular yarns" to give the β fibre
diagram: stretched denatured edestin and other seed globulins gave
the normal β-diagram, but we were very surprised to see that in the
photographs given by stretched strips of "poached" egg-white the
so-called "backbone reflection" at 4·65 Å was transposed from the
equator to the meridian, and we could only interpret this in terms
of bundles of β-chains so much thicker than the chains were long
that the act of extension tended to leave the latter lying not along
but across the direction of extension.[9] This X-ray photograph of
poached egg-white stretched at room temperature is shown in Fig.
1 (a), and is to be compared with Fig. 1 (b), a normal β-photo-
graph, taken for this article, of poached egg-white stretched in
steam.

Meanwhile, investigations on supercontraction went on and have
in fact been continued, especially with keratin, right up to the present
time by a number of people—Woods, Whewell, Mercer, Sikorski,
Peacock and others;[10] but in those early days the issue was con-
fused, as we know now, by disorientation effects, and it was Rudall
who first cleared up the X-ray side of the matter.[11] In his studies of
epidermin, the fibrous protein he had extracted from the epidermis,
and other members of the k–m–e–f group, he showed how the
"cross-β" diagram as he called it, to distinguish it from the "parallel-
β" diagram in which the 4·65 Å reflection lies on the equator,
could be revealed by re-stretching the supercontracted form, and he
pointed out in 1941 that it was just the kind of thing that was required to give X-ray substance to the view that supercontraction
resulted from the polypeptide chains falling into long transverse

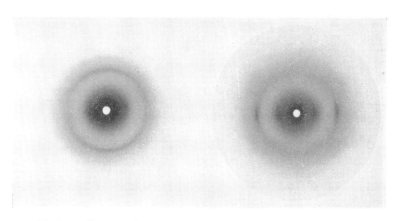

(a) X-ray diagram of a strip of "poached" egg-white stretched at room temperature by about 100%.

(b) X-ray diagram of the same stretched by about 200% in steam (Beighton). (Direction of stretching and fibre axis parallel to the long edge of the page.)

Fig. 1

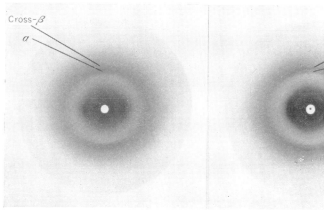

(a) X-ray diagram given by a partially supercontracted strip of oriented epidermis.

(b) X-ray diagram of a thin film, photographed with the beam parallel to the surface, of flagella of *B. subtilis*.

Fig. 2

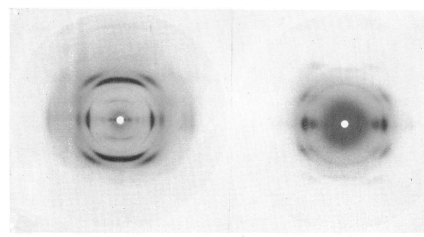

X-ray fibre diagrams of the egg-stalk of the lace-wing fly *Chrysopa*:
(*a*) in the natural cross-β form;   (*b*) in the parallel-β form pro-
and   duced from (*a*) by stretching.
(Rudall.)

FIG. 3

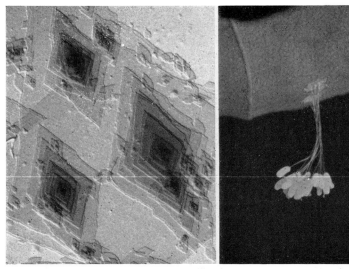

(*a*) Electron micrograph of the   (*b*) *Chrysopa* eggs suspended by
linear polyethylene "Marlex   their stalks from basal pede-
50" crystallized from trichlor-   stals (Millard).
ethylene (Keller).

FIG. 4

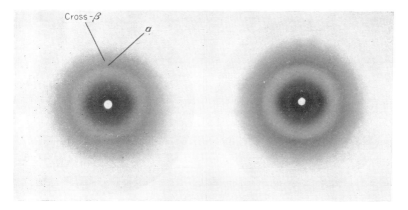

(a) X-ray diagram of a thin film prepared from actomyosin gel contracted by the action of adenosine triphosphate (Pautard);

(b) ditto of a thin film of actomyosin gel dried down at neutrality, then treated for 48 hrs at pH 5, washed again at neutrality, dried, and oriented by stretching (Pautard).

FIG. 6

folds. He also showed how the cross-β form may be reconverted to the α-form by the action of saturated urea, for instance.

And looking back again to the globular-to-fibrous protein experiments and the cross-β diagram obtained with stretched denatured egg-white, a clue as to its interpretation can be detected in a 1943 paper by Palmer and Galvin.[12] On re-examining their published X-ray diagram for the first stage of their production of fibres from denatured crystalline egg-albumin it is seen that there is a faint but definite tendency towards the cross-β pattern, which gives place to a well-oriented parallel-β pattern only after a second stretching in live steam. The authors do not mention this, but it is a clear enough indication now, in the light of the intramolecular transformations of the k–m–e–f group and the newer evidence reviewed below, of what lay at the heart of our own exploratory findings with egg-white: from the egg-albumin molecule too, on denaturation, there is liberated or formed first a transversely-folded ("supercontracted") configuration before the chains can finally be pulled out into the parallel-β configuration.

Thus there was building up, and in especial relation to the properties of myosin and the problem of muscle, a pretty sound case for not merely two but *three* definite polypeptide configurations of the k–m–e–f group: the normal α-configuration was only an intermediate state, as it were, being susceptible both of lengthening to the parallel-β configuration and of shortening to the cross-β configuration. Of recent years this case has been brought to essential completion, and the whole issue re-vitalized, by the discovery of naturally-occurring, as opposed to laboratory-produced, examples of the cross-β form, and of analogous transversely-folded states even in synthetic chain-molecules such as polyethylene. The first direct evidence of a natural cross-β configuration was found in X-ray diagrams of bacterial flagella[13]—a $4 \cdot 65$ Å meridional reflection not alone either, but superimposed on an α-pattern with an axial macro-period of about 410 Å as well, like that of skeletal muscle.[8] This combination, of course, as explained above, represents what we had all along been postulating as the ultimate molecular basis of muscular activity; no wonder then that we described bacterial flagella as of the nature of *monomolecular* muscles and suggested with increased confidence that the rhythmic localized shortening and lengthening implied by their bending movements rest too on an interchange between the α- and supercontracted configurations. From this viewpoint bacterial flagella stand for the muscle machine at its barest. They are only about 120 Å thick but, activated each from its basal granule, they comprise all that is really required, all that is basically necessary to explain.

The composite character of the X-ray diagram given by bacterial flagella is illustrated in Fig. 2, where it is matched against a mixed α and cross-β diagram given by a partially supercontracted strip of oriented epidermin prepared by Rudall.

There is admittedly a considerable element of speculation still in this interpretation of bacterial flagella, but not so with the structure of the egg-stalk of the green lace-wing fly *Chrysopa*, which Rudall and Parker have shown to be made up of polypeptide chains lying quite definitely in β-like folds transverse to the fibre axis.[14] This "jumping-cracker" or "grid-iron" configuration, so to call it, gives rise to the remarkably fine cross-β diagram reproduced in Fig. 3 (a), but on stretching it passes over into the parallel-β configuration, Fig. 3 (b), which is the normal state of other natural silks. The change is *not* simply another example of elongation by the more familiar process of orienting chain-bundles or micelles; it is a genuine intramolecular transformation corresponding formally to a transition from the supercontracted to the fully-extended state of the k–m–e–f group, though apparently without stopping at the intermediate α-state.

Furthermore, X-ray photographs of the "basal pedestal" of the egg-stalk, the film of protein spread by the laying insect on the underside of a leaf before it proceeds to draw off the actual thread (about 15–20 μ thick), show β-like polypeptide chains standing also *perpendicular* to the film, with the a and c axes in the plane of the film. The structural units of the fibre are therefore lying down already in the long "jumping-cracker" form, and are drawn off like that.

And now another seal is set on all these findings, and their implications widened immensely, by Keller's discovery that polyethylene (and other chain-polymers such as nylon) can build comparatively large orthodox crystals just as if they were short-chain hydrocarbons or fatty acids.[15] They do this by the free-energetically more favourable device of folding into much shorter lengths; instead of lying down fully extended they too assume the "jumping-cracker" form, a chain of regular transverse folds that in polyethene, for instance, are shown by additional X-ray reflections at low angles to be of the order of 100 Å long. Crystallites of the linear polyethylene "Marlex 50" as seen in the electron microscope, and in which the 100 Å folds stand perpendicular to the lozenge-shaped basal plane (001), simulating uniform single chains of that length, are illustrated in Fig. 4 (a). They are the hydrocarbon counterpart of the *Chrysopa* basal pedestals illustrated for comparison in Fig. 4 (b); and corresponding to the additional low-angle reflections given by polyethylene, there are to be seen on the equator of Fig. 3 (a) low-angle reflections which are additional to the high-angle pattern that is the transverse equivalent of the parallel-β pattern given by other silk fibroins.

So at last it must be accepted beyond all reasonable doubt that supercontraction in myosin (and other members of the k–m–e–f group) is no vague disorientation effect; it speaks out clearly now for the existence of a new polypeptide configuration shorter than the α-configuration, and more than ever must it be reckoned with in trying to uncover the fundamental molecular event in muscle contraction.[16] The question of the precise form of the supercontracted fold likewise becomes more pressing, the solution required being one which could apply to proteins in general but which achieves a special perfection in the structure of the egg-stalk silk of *Chrysopa*. We have recently arrived at such a solution that at the time of writing seems to be of great promise. The details are in process of being worked out and will be published elsewhere,[26] but the gist of the matter may already be put on record here with the help of the diagrammatic representation shown in Fig. 5.

From scale models constructed from planar amide groups hydrogen-bonded in the anti-parallel "pleated-sheet" fashion of Pauling and Corey (except at each 180° bend, where the hydrogen bond is non-linear as in the 7-membered ring of the 2_7 fold of Huggins and others), it is evident at once how the terminal bend of each transverse fold can form two excellent hydrogen bonds with the bends of two adjacent folds at the level below. If there are n residues between successive bends in the same chain, the resultant average strain per hydrogen bond will be reduced to only about $0·5/n$ kcal, which in general will be insignificant, and especially so in the case of the *Chrysopa* egg-stalk, with its very high proportion (about

40%) of serine residues, which must undoubtedly form strong side-chain linkages between the sheets of transverse folds as they pile on top of one another to build up the crystallographic third dimension. In Fig. 5 these sheets are to be thought of as extending laterally by a repetition of similar "steps", because it can be shown that the number of residues between one bend say on the left and the next on the right must be *odd* and that the completed transverse folds, viewed in the direction of the fibre axis, then take on the so-called "chair" form. In the *Chrysopa* structure it would appear for the moment that there are nine residues between bends, the residue at

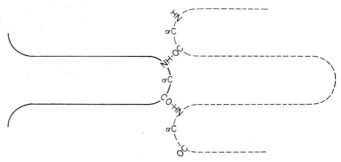

FIG. 5. Diagrammatic representation of the proposed cross-β fold and its stabilization by hydrogen-bonding to two adjacent folds at the level below.

each bend being a glycine flanked on one side by another glycine. On this basis the limiting extensibility, from the cross-β to the parallel-β configuration, should be to about $6\frac{1}{2}$ times the length of the former, which is roughly what is observed.

The cross-β diagrams so far obtained from the supercontracted configurations of the k–m–e–f group and egg albumin are not so informative as the *Chrysopa* diagram, but the interpretation is much the same in essentials. With keratin and myosin the observed elongation from fully supercontracted to fully extended also falls within the same kind of range—say to four or five times the supercontracted length—suggesting five to seven residues from one bend to the next. (Five residues would give an elongation of about 3·6, six about 4·3, and seven about 5.) Possibly, since the cross-β reflection appears to be always more disoriented than in the *Chrysopa* diagram, several fold-lengths can occur.

This order of length now suggested for the supercontracted fold in the k–m–e–f group is smaller than what was sometimes envisaged in the early days, but perhaps after all it is not unexpected if only from entropy considerations: *long* straight runs either transversely or longitudinally become increasingly less probable whether or not specific chemical factors intervene.

It is not really to be wondered at, either, that no cross-β diagram has yet been obtained from physiologically contracted muscle. The experimental conditions are very unfavourable, but besides that, chemical indications are that only part of the actomyosin complex is involved in contraction proper, another part at least being engaged in ATP-ase activity. We exploit the possibilities to the full when we supercontract isolated myosin (or muscle itself) by raising the temperature throughout, but for the relatively small shortening usually observed under physiological conditions it seems reasonable to think of the phenomenon as confined primarily to some special region. In other words, though we take full *in vitro* supercontraction of myosin and muscle, and the development of the cross-β diagram, as representative of and giving the clue to the effect in its more generalized connection, it is rather now to *Chrysopa* that we look to visualize the probably very precise configurational change to which physiological muscle contraction is normally restricted.

It requires water no warmer than about 40° to start myosin or muscle contracting *in vitro*, and the shortening becomes rapid in hotter water.[6] The counterpart *in vivo* of this thermal supply of contractile energy is presumably a more localized liberation from the ATP reaction, and fundamentally, according to the latest findings, this involves the transfer at each active site of one or more protons.[17] P. T. Speakman[18] has given reasons, from studies on wool, for thinking that this proton-transfer "trigger" initiating the "shaking-down" of the chains by the ATP energy outburst acts by provoking a wave of instability along the succession of internal hydrogen bonds of the α-helix.

It has been a handicap for the X-ray physicist, trying to persuade the physiologist how muscle works at the polypeptide-chain level, that he (the physicist) has had to argue so long by analogy with relatively crude experiments seemingly remote from the conditions prevailing in the living tissue, but the reproach has suddenly become considerably blunted, during only the last few months, by Pautard's demonstration[19] in our laboratory of distinct cross-β effects, if not in physiologically acceptable muscle, at least in actomyosin under the action of the physiological muscle reagent-in-chief, ATP. The experiment is illustrated in Fig. 6 (a); and what is probably still more to the point, in view of the evidence just mentioned for the part played by proton transfer in muscle contraction, this diagram can now be matched and supported by Fig. 6 (b), which illustrates Pautard's further demonstration[20] of incipient cross-β formation in actomyosin simply by lowering the pH below 6.

Altogether, we have recently come to feel that the supercontraction and cross-β interpretation of muscular activity has reached the stage where it has to be reckoned with very seriously indeed, in spite of its apparent divorce from, if not actual conflict with, Huxley's conclusion from electron microscopy that whether a skeletal muscle contracts or elongates there is involved no final change in the *lengths* of the interdigitating myosin and actin filaments but only a change in the *extent* of interdigitation.[21] This gap between the two approaches must, of course, be bridged before ever we can feel truly confident that we are at last along the right lines. But is there any real gap—any gap, that is, beyond the present inability of the electron microscope to reveal what takes place at the moment of contraction? It shows the structure only before and after contraction (or elongation) but throws no light on the process between. The latter could very well resemble the movements of the geometer caterpillar as it proceeds by alternately drawing itself up into a loop and then straightening itself out again. According to this idea, the caterpillar would seem to correspond with the actin filaments alternately looping and slipping straight again in response to the myosin filaments alternately contracting and relaxing.

However that may be, it cannot be repeated too often that it is possible to be obsessed with the highly specialized structure and workings of skeletal muscle and thereby lose sight of the problem in its less complicated manifestations. We would draw attention again particularly to the bacterial flagellum, which comprises the basic features of muscular activity all within the compass of a single macromolecule. Once we get to the bottom of that—and this article is meant to suggest the way—many of the difficulties associated with higher muscles will be seen as mere elaborations.

It will be good to conclude with a few remarks on what may be called the corpuscle-fibre paradox in fine-structural studies of muscle and other biological fibres[16]—the curious situation that whereas man-made fibres, as the result of lessons learned first from natural fibres, are "molecular yarns" spun from more or less drawn-out chain-molecules, it appears now that at least the initial stages in the construction of natural fibres often involve a stringing-together of unit "beads" of coiled-up chains. A classical early, and still outstanding, indication was given by feather keratin, but since then there have been, for example: Waugh's fibrous insulin, Bailey's tropomyosin, Straub's F-actin, and—most arresting in relation to our discussion here—Andrew Szent-Györgyi's "protomyosins", units weighing only about 5,000 into which he has succeeded in splitting myosin by nothing more drastic than the action of urea, under certain specific conditions.[22] One of the very best illustrations of the fibre–corpuscle question can be observed with flagella detached from the alga *Polytoma*, which, simply on drying a preparation for examination in the electron microscope, disintegrate first into the familiar eleven sub-fibrils, next into filaments, then finally into chains of particles of diameter about 175 Å.[8, 16]

Albert Szent-Györgyi[23] supposes that since even the myosin "molecule" thus turns out in the end to be no other than strings of particles held together by secondary forces, contraction must mean the collapse, somehow, of such strings into shorter, fatter groupings. All the same, the fact remains that myosin also behaves like a long-range elastic "molecular yarn" constructed from polypeptide chains normally in the α-configuration but which can be stretched into the parallel-β configuration and supercontracted into the cross-β configuration; and to harmonize these two descriptions dynamically is the problem. Various people have put forward the concept of regular linear sequences of packets of suitably coiled-up polypeptides as a simultaneous explanation in a more static sense of both the apparent biogenesis and the X-ray diagrams of natural protein fibres, but the tendency has been at the same time to think of the globular proteins as mostly all-or-none structures, so to speak, ready to unfold irreversibly at the slightest provocation; and from there it was not so easy to go on to explain long-range biological contractility—at any rate, not so easy as in terms of the folding and unfolding of the chain-molecules of straightforward molecular yarns which the X-ray diagrams originally suggested, perfectly correctly in the case of many fibre structures. Now, however, we know from, for instance, the optical studies of Doty and his collaborators that the presence of α-configurational components can be revealed not only in the fibrous proteins where they were first discovered by X-ray diffraction, but in the make-up of orthodox globular proteins too; and, moreover, *the proportions of these α-components can be reversibly altered to some extent by suitably altering the environment.* The desired dynamic co-ordination must therefore surely be this, that these intraglobular configurational changes will, in principle, be accompanied by shape changes and changes in the direction and mode of contact with adjacent corpuscles, leading thence, in a linear polymer, to spiralization and overall length changes, and conceivably marked length changes to boot.[16]

The mitotic cycle of chromosomes provides the classic example of the spiralization of chains of biological particles at the visual level, and in a closely similar connection Ambrose, with the help of the interference microscope, has recently obtained most impressive pictures of the way in which minute fibrils are formed by the linear aggregation of intracellular particles, and of how readily these fibrils fall then into helical configurations.[24] And down at the protein molecular level particularly nice evidence of the kind is seen in Bresler's findings with human serum albumin[25]—how the axial ratio of the molecule, considered as an ellipsoid, increases progressively from 4 to 16 when the water + dioxane solvent at pH 10 is made more and more hydrophobic by increasing the dioxane concentration; this takes place, indeed, without any change in the optical rotation, and so probably by modifying only the tertiary structure, without affecting the α-helical components. The inference is clearly that chains of serum albumin, if there were such things, would be susceptible of violent contortions.

REFERENCES

1. W. T. ASTBURY and A. STREET, *Phil. Trans. Roy. Soc.* A **230**, 75 (1931).
2. W. T. ASTBURY and H. J. WOODS, *Phil. Trans. Roy Soc.* A **232**, 333 (1933).
3. See, for example, L. PAULING and R. B. COREY, *Proc. Roy. Soc.* B **141**, 21 (1953).
4. F. H. C. CRICK, *Nature* **170**, 882 (1952); *Acta Cryst.* **6**, 689 (1953); L. PAULING and R. B. COREY, *Nature* **171**, 59 (1953).

5. See, for example, W. T. ASTBURY, On the structure of biological fibres and the problem of muscle, *Proc. Roy. Soc.* B **134**, 303 (1947) (Croonian Lecture, 1945).
6. W. T. ASTBURY and S. DICKINSON, *Proc. Roy. Soc.* B **129**, 307 (1940).
7. W. T. ASTBURY, *Nature* **160**, 388 (1947); *Exptl. Cell Res.*, Suppl. I, 235 (1949).
8. W. T. ASTBURY, E. BEIGHTON, and C. WEIBULL, *Symp. Soc. Exptl. Biol.* **9**, 282 (1955).
9. W. T. ASTBURY, S. DICKINSON, and K. BAILEY, *Biochem. J.* **29**, 2351 (1935).
10. For selected references see, for example, N. PEACOCK, *Biochim. Biophys. Acta* **32**, 220 (1959).
11. K. M. RUDALL, Symp. on Fibrous Proteins, *J. Soc. Dyers & Colourists*, p. 15 (1946); *Advances in Protein Chemistry* **7**, 255 (1952).
12. K. J. PALMER and J. A. GALVIN, *J. Am. Chem. Soc.* **65**, 2187 (1943).
13. W. T. ASTBURY and C. WEIBULL, *Nature* **163**, 280 (1949).
14. K. D. PARKER and K. M. RUDALL, *Nature* **179**, 905 (1957).
15. See, for example, A. KELLER and A. O'CONNOR, *Disc. Faraday Soc.*, No. 25, 114 (1958).
16. W. T. ASTBURY, *Disc. Faraday Soc.*, No. 25, 80 (1958).
17. M. C. GOODALL, *Nature* **182**, 677 (1958).
18. P. T. SPEAKMAN, *Nature* **184**, 339 (1959).
19. F. G. E. PAUTARD, *Nature* **182**, 788 (1958).
20. F. G. E. PAUTARD, *Nature* **183**, 1391 (1959).
21. H. E. HUXLEY, *J. Biophys. and Biochem. Cytol.* **3**, 631 (1957); also reference 4 in Introduction to this volume.
22. A. G. SZENT-GYÖRGYI and M. BORBIRO, *Arch. Biochem. Biophys.* **60**, 180 (1956).
23. A. SZENT-GYÖRGYI, *Science* **124**, 873 (1956); *J. Cell. Comp. Physiol.* **49**, Suppl. 1, 311 (1957).
24. E. J. AMBROSE, *Proc. Roy. Soc.* B **148**, 57 (1957).
25. S. E. BRESLER, *Disc. Faraday Soc.*, No. 25, 158 (1958).
26. W. T. ASTBURY, E. BEIGHTON and K. D. PARKER, *Biochem. Biophys. Acta* **35**, 17 (1959)

4

INFLUENCE OF HYDROGEN-ION AND SALT CONCENTRATION ON POLYELECTROLYTES

by J. A. V. BUTLER

Chester Beatty Research Institute, London

I SHALL discuss the effects of pH and salt concentration on the shape and size of polyelectrolyte particles, but although, as we shall see, these variables produce very marked effects, I must say at the outset that I do not think that these effects have more than an indirect connection with the situation in muscle, which is of a much higher degree of complication.

Polyelectrolytes are long chain polymers, in which many of the groups are capable of being ionized, so that in the ionized state there will be free charges at frequent intervals along the chain. Some examples, both natural and synthetic, are shown in Fig. 1. As a result of this the physical properties in solution are to a great degree dependent on the state of ionization of the polymer; and moreover interactions both between the particles themselves and their counter ions and with added salts have a very marked effect. The dissociation of a polyelectrolyte itself differs from that of simple electrolytes owing to the constraints resulting from the concentration of dissociable groups along the polymer chain. The behaviour of each ionizable group is to a great extent influenced by the close proximity of its neighbours. A result of this is that it becomes progressively more difficult to remove further ions as the charge on the polymer ion increases, so that the final stages of ionization of polymer salt become increasingly difficult. Another consequence is that in the charged state, the charges carried by the polymer ion repel each other and thus tend to get as far as they can from each other. The result is an expansion of flexible polymer particles as ionization proceeds.

The simplest measure of the size of a polymer particle is its reduced viscosity. If the viscosity of a solution (concentration c) is η and that of the solvent η_0; the reduced viscosity is:

$$\eta_{red.} = \frac{\eta - \eta_0}{\eta_0 c}$$

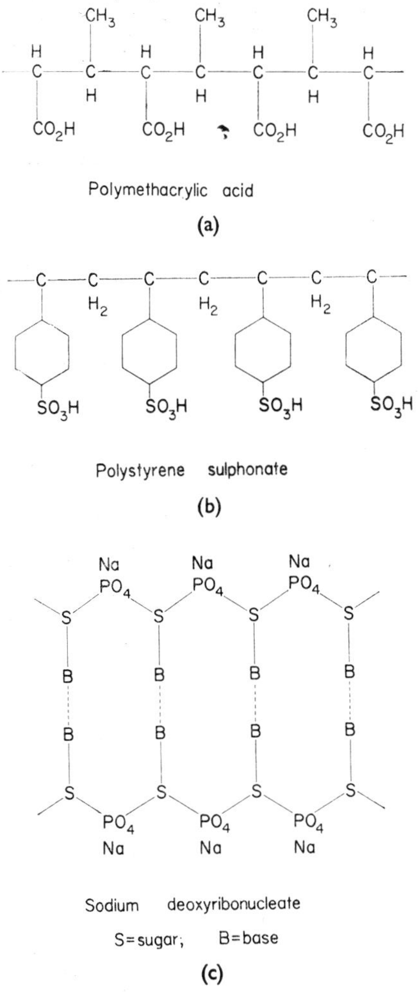

Polymethacrylic acid

(a)

Polystyrene sulphonate

(b)

Sodium deoxyribonucleate

S = sugar; B = base

(c)

Fig. 1. Some typical polyelectrolytes.

At zero concentration this becomes the intrinsic viscosity

$$[\eta] = \left(\frac{\eta - \eta_0}{\eta_0 c} \right)_{c \to 0}$$

Early measurements on reduced viscosities of some polyelectrolyte solutions were made by Fuoss and Strauss,[1] who found that the reduced viscosity was greatly dependent on the state of ionization of the polymer (as determined by the pH) and also for a given state of ionization on the salt concentration (Fig. 2). With no added salt,

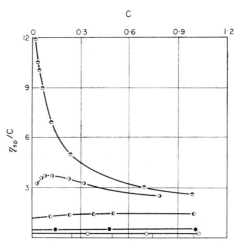

FIG. 2.   Reduced viscosity of polyvinyl butyl pyridonium chloride in water and solutions of KBr. (C = grams polyelectrolyte in 100 cc of solution.) (Fuoss and Strauss[1].)
The upper curve is that in water alone, the others with increasing concentrations of KBr.

the reduced viscosity increases steadily as the dilution increases. This is attributed to the volume of the polymer particle increasing as its electrolytic dissociation is increased by increasing the dilution. It should reach a maximum when the particle is fully extended and this has been observed in a number of cases.[2] But even very small concentrations of added salts markedly decrease the viscosity. This has been attributed to an increasing association of "counter ions" with the polymer particle, as a result of which the mutual electrical repulsion of the charges of the polymer chain is diminished. This is often referred to as a "shielding action" of the counter ions on the charges of the chain, but it is more probably due to the actual diminution of the charge on the polymer in the presence of added ions of opposite sign.

Some polyelectrolytes are much more sensitive to salts than others. An example of extreme sensitivity is sodium polystyrene sulphonate investigated by Butler, Robins and Shooter.[2] Here the

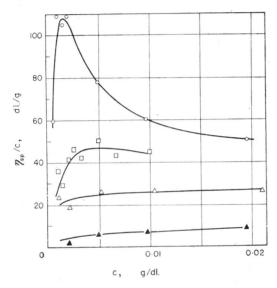

FIG. 3. Reduced viscosity plotted against concentration for aqueous and saline solutions of polystyrene sulphonate.

○ conductivity water;	□ 5×10^{-5} M NaCl;
△ 7×10^{-4} M NaCl;	▲ 8×10^{-3} M NaCl.

addition of less than 10^{-3} M NaCl is sufficient to reduce the viscosity to about one half of that in the absence of added salts (Fig. 3).

It was also found that the degree of ionization of the polymer when present as a free acid is to a large extent independent of the polymer concentration. This means that the dissociation of hydrogen ions from a single acid grouping depends on the ratio acid/salt in the polymer chain, but is not determined by the concentration of polymer particles in solution. It is thus the micro-environment at a given site along the polymer chain which determines the dissociation behaviour.

We can now turn to polyelectrolytes having a rigid structure, of which the best known example is the naturally occurring substance, deoxyribonucleic acid, which has the form of a fairly rigid rod, the ionizable groups being phosphates arranged in spirals round the

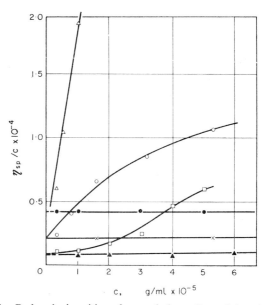

FIG. 4. Reduced viscosities of several deoxyribonucleic acids. The horizontal lines showed measurements at similar concentrations in sodium chloride (0·1 N) solutions (BUTLER, CONWAY and JAMES, *Trans. Faraday Soc.* **50**, 612, 1954).

rod, the separation along the rod direction of adjacent phosphate groups being 3·4 Å.

The behaviour of this substance is quite different from that of the flexible chains already considered. The reduced viscosity in water increases steadily with the concentration of the polyelectrolyte (Fig. 4).

Solutions of the sodium salt of deoxyribonucleic acid also, in general, show a marked dependence of the viscosity on the concentration of added salts. However, it was found by Pouyet[3] and by Conway and Butler,[4] that this dependence diminishes as the concentration is decreased and becomes practically zero at zero concentration (Fig. 4). This means that when the particles are well separated from each other, the addition of salt has no effect on their size. The increase of reduced viscosity as the concentration is increased must be due to the interaction of the particles and it follows that the effect of added ions is to reduce the amount of this interaction.

With regard to the nature of the interaction, it is evidently due to some kind of electrical forces between the ions and the particles. There is some doubt as to the nature of these forces. A direct interaction of the Debye–Hückel kind between the charged particles and their counter ions has been envisaged;[5] but the working out of its consequences presents great difficulty. Another way of accounting for the interaction is to suppose[6] that it arises from the repulsion of similarly charged particles, as calculated by Verwey and Overbeek.[7] The effect of such repulsion will be to limit the volume of the solution into which the polyelectrolyte particles can enter and this limitation will contribute a component to the viscosity of the solution. Now the effect of increasing the ionic strength of the solution is to reduce the thickness of the double layer round the particle[8]; and this will reduce the degree of interaction owing to the decrease in the excluded volume.

It is evident from the above that there are a number of ways in which the configuration in a system of ionizable polyelectrolyte particles can be modified by changes of pH and salt concentration. Of course in a solution of dispersed particles there is no means of converting such changes into mechanical work. However, if the polyelectrolyte particles are joined together in a framework by some kind of cross-links, they will form a polyelectrolyte gel in which changes of configuration of the polyelectrolyte particle will result in a change in the space occupied by the whole gel and such a system can be arranged so that mechanical work is done when the gel swells. A system of this kind was investigated by Ambrose and Butler.[9] This consisted of films of a nucleoprotein, which is insoluble in water under some conditions. In water it swells to a size several times that in the dry state; but in salt solutions the swelling is inhibited to an extent which depends primarily on the ionic strength.

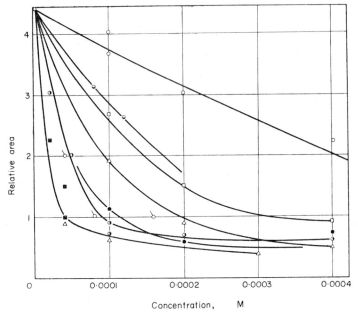

FIG. 5. Effect of small concentrations of metal salts on swelling of "native" thymus nucleoprotein films (AMBROSE and BUTLER, *Disc. Faraday Soc.* No. 13, 261, 1953).

—O— alkali chlorides	—◐— AgNO₃	—□— MgCl₂
—●— CaCl₂	—▽— ZnSO₄	—△— FeCl₃
—■— Th(NO₃)₄	—◑— LaCl₃	—⊖— Pb(NO₃)₂

This again could be interpreted as due to repulsion between the particles being diminished by added electrolytes (Fig. 5).

This will give an idea of the possibilities of converting chemical into mechanical energy in very simple systems by variations of the pH or the salt concentration.

REFERENCES

1. R. M. FUOSS and U. P. STRAUSS, *J. Polymer Sci.* 3, 602 (1948); cf. O. T. F. PALS and J. J. HERMANS, *Rec. trav. chim., Pays Bas* 71, 488 (1952).
2. P. ALEXANDER and S. F. HITCH, *Biochem. Biophys. Acta* 9, 229 (1952). J. A. V. BUTLER, A. B. ROBINS, and K. V. SHOOTER, *Proc. Roy. Soc. A* 241, 299 (1957).
3. J. POUYET, *J. Chim. Phys.* 48, 49 (1951).
4. B. E. CONWAY and J. A. V. BUTLER, *J. Polymer. Sci.* 12, 199 (1954).

5. J. A. V. Butler, B. E. Conway, and D. W. F. James, *Trans. Faraday Soc.* **50**, 612 (1954).
6. J. A. V. Butler and B. E. Conway, *La Ricerca Scientifica, Symposio Internazionale de Chemica Macromolare*, 1955.
7. E. J. W. Verwey and J. Overbeek, *Theory of the Stability of Lyophobic Colloids*, Elsevier, Amsterdam.
8. L. Onsager, *Ann. N.Y. Acad. Sci.* **51**, 627 (1949).
9. E. J. Ambrose and J. A. V. Butler, *Disc. Faraday Soc.*, No. 13, 261 (1953)

5

INFLUENCE OF COUNTERIONS ON MOLECULAR WEIGHT AND SHAPE OF A POLYELECTROLYTE

by R. E. COOPER and A. WASSERMANN

*William Ramsay and Ralph Forster Laboratories,
University College, London*

SUMMARY

The weight average molecular weights, M_W, the interaction constants, B, the viscosity numbers $[\eta]$ and the electrical equivalent conductance, Λ, of sodium, potassium and magnesium alginates have been measured. On passing from sodium or potassium alginate to the magnesium salt, M_W increases substantially, B and Λ decrease, while $[\eta]$ does not change markedly. These observations were made when magnesium alginate was prepared in the gel phase, where alginate chains are close together. If the replacement of sodium by magnesium ions occurred in dilute solution, a different magnesium alginate was obtained, the M_W value of which was not much larger than that of sodium alginate. It is assumed that magnesium ions are capable of combining with carboxylate groups of the alginate, thereby forming inter- and intra-molecular cross links and that the molecular weights and related properties of magnesium alginate depend on the relative number of the two types of bonds, which in turn is influenced by the concentration conditions prevailing during the sodium magnesium ion exchange. An equilibrium mixture of the two types of magnesium alginate was not established under the specified experimental conditions. This indicates localized counterion fixation involving bonds of greater stability than that usually attributed to salt bridges in aqueous solution. Ion pair formation of this kind may account also for the small Λ values of magnesium alginate.

INTRODUCTION

VISCOMETRIC investigations of solutions containing poly-acids,[1, 2] polybases[3] or polyampholytes[4] have shown that the molecular shape of these polyelectrolytes depends on the hydrogen ion concentration. It could be established,[5] furthermore, that the pH influences also macroscopic properties of fibres made from the same poly-acids, the solution behaviour of which had been studied in separate experiments. Some of these effects can be regarded as a confirmation of a hypothesis due to Meyer.[6]

Under biological conditions, polyelectrolytes are frequently in contact with buffered solutions. It is important, therefore, to find out whether stoicheiometrically well defined, simple and reversible reactions, which do not involve an alteration of pH, are also capable of producing shape changes of polyelectrolytes on a molecular and macroscopic level. For this reason, solutions of sodium alginate[7] and fibres[8] made from various alginates have been studied and it was found that the replacement of polyvalent by monovalent counterions affects the molecular shape of the alginate, which in turn influences the small angle X-ray scattering, macroscopic length, birefringence and elastic properties of the fibres. The effects are due to the rupture of cross links, formed by polyvalent counterions,

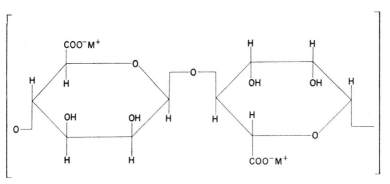

FIG. 1. Repeating unit of alginates: the symbol M^+ indicated a univalent counterion.

between adjacent alginate chains; and they can be interpreted as an isothermal "melting" of ordered zones. This is comparable to the non-isothermal shrinkage of collagen,[9] contraction or super-contraction of oriented specimens of keratin, epidermis proteins or fibrin[10] and to the dimensional change of fibrous natural rubber[11] and polythene.[12]

These experiments are mentioned because they show that it is of interest to compare the solution properties of a poly-acid, fully neutralized by mono- and polyvalent counter ions. Such an investigation is now described. As in the earlier work,[7, 8] the polyelectrolyte was an alginate, a repeating unit[13] of which is shown in Fig. 1. The counterions were sodium, potassium and magnesium.

The latter was chosen because magnesium alginate is water soluble, like the sodium and potassium salts, while most other alginates, containing polyvalent counterions, are insoluble gels. Similar precipitates are formed if other polyacids are completely neutralized with bivalent cations.[14]

EXPERIMENTAL

Potassium alginate was made by treating solid sodium alginate with 2 M potassium acetate and by subsequent dialysis against aqueous acetone.[15] Three types of magnesium alginate were prepared. (1) Solid sodium alginate was treated with 2 M magnesium acetate, the alginate concentration, during the ion exchange, being about 7 g-equiv./l. gel; dialysis was done as above and the magnesium alginate, free of permeant ions,* was precipitated with acetone and dried in vacuo at 20°. Repeated analyses[15] showed that the ratio equivalent carboxyl/equivalent magnesium was $1 \cdot 00 \pm 0 \cdot 03$. (2) Solutions of magnesium alginate, type 1, either in water or in $0 \cdot 01 - 0 \cdot 04$ M magnesium chloride, containing about $0 \cdot 4$ g alginate per 100 ml., were centrifuged for 4 hours at 2×10^4 g and 20°. The supernatant solution, containing magnesium alginate of lower molecular weight than samples of type 1, was removed with a special pipette, which did not stir up a small quantity of a high molecular weight fraction at the bottom of the centrifuge tube. (3) Aqueous solutions of sodium alginate, containing $0 \cdot 1 - 0 \cdot 3$ equivalents/litre, were dialysed against $0 \cdot 01 - 0 \cdot 04$ M magnesium chloride. Several samples of each of these three types of magnesium alginate were prepared and investigated. The sodium alginate used for all these experiments was the same specimen as that described in the earlier work.[7, 8]

The molecular weights, M_W, the interaction constants, B, and the radii of gyration, ρ, of the alginates were deduced from light scattering, direct transmission and refractive index increment measurements, made respectively with a Brice–Pheonix instrument, a Unicam spectrophotometer and a Rayleigh interferometer. The solution here considered are three component systems, and, there-

---

* Here and below "permeant" refers to electrolytes which can be removed from the alginate solution by dialysis. The counterions which are required to neutralize the alginate cannot be dialysed and are "non-permeant".

fore, a correction factor calculated from results of membrane equilibrium measurements had to be applied.

Solutions of sodium, potassium and magnesium alginates of types 2 and 3 were freed from dust by high speed centrifugation. Magnesium alginate of type 1 could not be treated in this way, because of fractionation, as mentioned above. Solutions of this material were either prepared from centrifuged dust-free reagents, or they were filtered through dust-free sintered glass filters of appropriate porosity. In one experiment, magnesium alginate of type 3 was prepared by introducing a centrifuged dust-free solution of sodium alginate into a suitably supported dialysis bag, which had been rinsed with a dust-free electrolyte solution, the dialysis being done in a closed container; solutions prepared in this way were not centrifuged but some of them were passed through a sintered glass filter. Shortly before the light scattering or direct transmission tests the purity of solutions was checked by observation through a magnifying glass at low angles, relative to the direction of an intense light beam, focused to the centre of the vessel.

Rayleigh ratios of sodium and potassium alginates were determined at three angles, the particle scattering factors and the relevant ρ values being calculated from the intrinsic dissymmetry, on the assumption that these solutes are polydisperse random coils. The M_W, B and ρ values of the magnesium alginates were calculated without making assumptions about the molecular shape. Turbidities of magnesium alginate, type 1, determined by direct transmission tests were measured at 9 wavelengths between 350 and 550 mμ; and Rayleigh ratios of these specimens and of the other two magnesium alginates were measured at two wavelengths for 12–14 angles in the range 135–25°. Tests with each wavelength and at each angle were done within a sufficiently large concentration range to enable an extrapolation to be made to zero concentration. The results of the membrane equilibrium measurements, intrinsic dissymmetries, typical wavelength dependence of turbidities, Zimm plots and details relating to the computation of M_W, B and ρ will be given elsewhere.

The electrical conductance was measured in a conventional a.c. bridge, operating at about 1,000 cycles/sec. The alginate solution had been dialysed against water, until the specific conductance of the water (4×10^{-6} Ω^{-1} cm^{-1} or less) remained unchanged. In some runs the outside solution contained "mixed" ion exchange resins of the type used for removing, in one stage, cationic and anionic impurities.

Viscosities were measured at $25 \cdot 0°$ in a Flory[16] and in a Couette instrument[17] which covered rate of shear ranges of respectively 2800–200 and 20–$0 \cdot 5$ sec^{-1}. If the ionic strength of the solvent was not too low and the alginate concentration not too high there was no detectable influence of the rate of shear. In solvents of relatively low ionic strength or in water, free of permeant electrolytes, the viscosity depended on the rate of shear,* but the limiting slope of viscosity against rate of shear curves was zero in all cases, in agreement with the hydronamic theories. All the viscosity numbers, $[\eta]$, discussed below relate to conditions in which a significant influence of the rate of shear does not occur. The alginate concentrations tested were between $0 \cdot 014$ and $0 \cdot 12$ g/100 ml. if the solvent contained permeant electrolytes. Reliable viscosity measurements with sodium and magnesium alginate, type 1, in pure water were made in the ranges $0 \cdot 00382$–$0 \cdot 0197$ and $0 \cdot 00492$–$0 \cdot 0538$ g/100 ml. For each determination of $[\eta]$ the reduced viscosity, η_{spec}/c, was determined at least for five concentrations.

RESULTS

Numerical values of the weight average molecular weights, M_W, and of the interaction constants, B, of these alginates are in columns 4 and 5 of Table 1. The three magnesium alginates were also characterized by ρ, their Z-average radii of gyration (column 6). These results were obtained by light scattering measurements. Tests with sodium alginate in $0 \cdot 500$ and $1 \cdot 00†$ M sodium chloride and with the three magnesium alginates in $0 \cdot 0100$, $0 \cdot 0300$ and $0 \cdot 0400*$ M magnesium chloride were also done. Comparison of these results with those listed in Table 1 showed that M_W, B and ρ were not significantly dependent on the ionic strength of the solution. Magnesium alginate, type 1, was reconverted into sodium alginate, by treatment with 2 M sodium acetate and subsequent dialysis. The M_W value of this sodium alginate, in $0 \cdot 1$ M sodium chloride, agreed,

---

* Calculations relating the observed rate of shear dependence to specified molecular shapes of these alginates will be reported elsewhere.

† Precipitation of alginate occurs if the concentration of sodium or magnesium chloride is higher than $1 \cdot 0$ or $0 \cdot 04$ M.

TABLE 1. WEIGHT AVERAGE MOLECULAR WEIGHTS, M_W, INTERACTION CONSTANTS, B, AND VISCOSITY NUMBERS, $[\eta]$, OF SODIUM, POTASSIUM AND MAGNESIUM ALGINATES

The latter solutes are also characterized by ρ,
the Z-average radius of gyration.

Alginate of	Solvent: aqueous solution of	Molarity of permeant chloride	$M_W \times 10^{-5}$ ($\sim 25°$)	$B \times 10^3$ $\left(\dfrac{\mathrm{ml} \times \mathrm{mol}}{\mathrm{g}^2} \sim 25°\right)$	$\rho \times 10^{-3}$ (A; 25°)	$[\eta]$ (100 ml. soln/g 25·0°)
Sodium	NaCl	0·100	1·4±0·3	1·0±0·3	—	9·4±0·2
Potassium	KCl	0·100	1·0±0·3	3·0±1·0	—	8·9±0·2
Magnesium,						
Type 1	⎫	⎫	400±100	⎫	1·6±0·3	7·5±0·2
Type 2	⎬ MgCl₂	⎬0·0200	12±2	⎬<0·2	1·6±0·3	7·3±0·2
Type 3	⎭	⎭	2·2±0·5	⎭	1·1±0·2	7·6±0·2

within $\pm 20\%$, with that in the first line of Table 1. The last column of Table 1 shows the viscosity number of these alginates, the solvents being the same as those used for the determination of M_W (see columns 2 and 3). Figures 2 and 3 show the equivalent electrical conductances of these alginates and the influence of the ionic strength, μ, of the solvent on the viscosity number $[\eta]$. In some of these latter experiments, the permeant electrolytes were sodium veronal buffer, $\mu = 0·00643$, pH $= 7·50$ and magnesium veronal buffer, $\mu = 0·00965$, pH $7·50$. The mode of plotting the results facilitates comparison with other polyelectrolytes.[3] The concentration dependence of the specific viscosity, η_{spec}, of these alginate solutions is given, as a first approximation, by[18]

$$\frac{\eta_{\mathrm{spec}}}{c} = [\eta] + k' \, [\eta]^2 \, c \qquad (1)$$

The constant k', determined with an accuracy of about 15% was in most cases between $0·4$ and $0·6$, both for sodium and magnesium alginate. An exception was sodium alginate in a solvent of $\mu = 0·00643$, where k' increased to about $1·7$. The reduced viscosities of sodium or magnesium alginate in pure water, free of

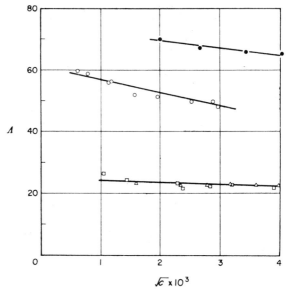

Fig. 2. Equivalent electrical conductance, Λ, of sodium, potassium and magnesium alginates in water; $25\cdot0°$. Λ in $\Omega^{-1} \times cm^2 \times$ g equiv.$^{-1}$ Alginate concentration, c, in g-equiv./ml.

○ sodium alginate
● potassium alginate
□ magnesium alginate, type 1
△ magnesium alginate, type 3

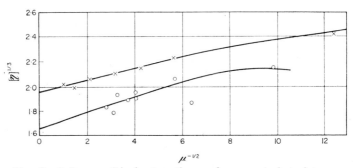

Fig. 3. Influence of ionic strength, μ, of permeant electrolytes on viscosity number, $[\eta]$, of sodium and magnesium alginate, $25\cdot0°$. $[\eta]$ in 100 ml./g.

× sodium alginate
○ magnesium alginate, type 1.

permeant electrolytes, increase rapidly with decreasing concentration.* In the specified concentration ranges the relationship[3]

$$\frac{\eta_{spec}}{c} = \frac{a}{1 + \beta c^{\frac{1}{2}}} \qquad (2)$$

holds. It could thus be established that $[\eta]$ of sodium and magnesium alginate is respectively 400 ± 40 and 170 ± 20 (concentration expressed in g per 100 ml.)

DISCUSSION

Donnan and Rose[20] determined viscosity numbers, $[\eta]$, of sodium alginate of different number average molecular weight, M_N, in $0 \cdot 1$ N sodium chloride and established the relationship $[\eta] = K M_N^{\gamma}$ with $\gamma = 1 \cdot 0 \pm 0 \cdot 1$.† Thus, sodium alginate behaves hydrodynamically like a chain-like polymer in which the solvent drainage is enhanced by a certain degree of stiffness and by the movement of counter ions in the polymer coil.[21]

On conversion into the magnesium salt a polymerization occurs, as shown by the molecular weight in the third line of the Table, which is, at least, 150 times larger than that in the first line. It is assumed that magnesium ions combine with carboxylate groups of the polymeric anions, thereby producing inter- and intramolecular cross links. In the latter case it has to be taken into account that adjacent carboxylate groups of an alginate molecule cannot combine with one and the same magnesium ion, for stereochemical reasons, but more distant carboxyl groups can react. Thus "loops" would be formed which pull the alginate chains together and produce a compact molecule. This explains why the viscosity number in the third line of Table 1 is somewhat smaller than that in the first line, although the molecular weight, M_W, of magnesium alginate, type 1, is so large; and why the radii of gyration of the magnesium alginates, types 1 and 2 are similar, notwithstanding the considerable difference between the M_W values.

* This effect is well known in sodium alginate solution[19] and in solutions of other polyelectrolytes.[1, 2, 3]

† Experiments completed after this paper had been submitted for publication show that the exponent γ' in the relationship $[\eta] = K'M_W^{\gamma'}$ (M_W = weight average molecular weight) is also $1 \cdot 0 \pm 0 \cdot 1$. It is possible, therefore, to compute $[\eta]$ magnesium alginate/$[\eta]$ sodium alginate for samples of the same M_W value. The ratios obtained are much smaller than unity and will be discussed elsewhere.

In preparing magnesium alginate, type 1, the replacement of sodium by magnesium ions was done in the gel phase, where adjacent alginate chains are close together, thereby favouring the formation of intermolecular magnesium carboxylate bonds. Magnesium alginate, type 3, on the other hand, was obtained in dilute solution, thus making the formation of intramolecular bonds more probable. One would expect, therefore, that the molecular weight of magnesium alginate, type 3, is lower. This has been observed (see Table 1).

The molecular weights of these magnesium alginates showed no significant drift (20°) within two or three days after their preparation and it can be concluded that an equilibrium mixture is not established under these conditions. This indicates localized counter ion fixation, possibly assisted by participation of some of the hydroxyl groups, shown in Fig. 1, thereby producing magnesium carboxylate hydroxy complexes, involving chelate rings of a stability greater than that of ordinary salt bridges, but not great enough to prevent the exchange of magnesium against other cations under suitable conditions.* Such magnesium carboxylate links are probably formed as the result of co-operative effects and they may be partly responsible for the relatively small electrical conductance† of magnesium alginate (Fig. 2); and they should make certain hydrodynamic properties of magnesium alginate comparable to those of branched polymers, which are characterized by relatively small interaction constants,[22] B values, and exponents,[23] γ', in the relation $[\eta] = K' M_W^{\gamma'}$. The figures in columns 4, 5 and 7 of Table 1 show that the B values of magnesium alginate are at least five times smaller than those of sodium or potassium alginate and that γ' is near to zero.

In other respects, however, magnesium alginate behaves like sodium or potassium alginate, for which localized counterion fixation is not postulated. The graphs in Fig. 3, relating to magnesium and sodium alginate, and corresponding relationships of other flexible polyelectrolytes neutralized by univalent counterions[3] are similar and the $[\eta]$ values of both magnesium and sodium alginate increase on passing from dilute salt solution to pure water

* The complex formation envisaged here need not necessarily have a counterpart in the interaction between magnesium ions and d-mannuronic or l-guluronic acid, the "monomers" of alginic acid.

† These conductances, together with results of transference measurements, obtained by D. P. Buchner will be discussed in another paper.

as the solvent. It is suggested that magnesium alginate contains counterions of two types; (a) those which are firmly bound to ionic sites of the polymeric anion and which give rise to relatively stable inter- and intra-molecular bonds; (b) those which behave like the univalent counterions of sodium or potassium alginate and which are responsible for the influence of the ionic strength on the viscosity numbers and for the concentration dependence of the reduced viscosity according to (2). These latter counterions, and intra-molecular magnesium carboxylate bonds, are made responsible for the solubility of magnesium alginate: if all magnesium ions required to neutralize the polymeric anions were of type (a) and formed intermolecular bonds, the critical gel point[24] would be reached and magnesium alginate would be insoluble.

We are grateful to Professor J. A. V. Butler, F.R.S., for placing the Couette Viscometer of the Chester Beatty Research Institute at our disposal, to Drs. R. Paine and A. B. Robins for assistance in its use, and to the Brighton Education Committee for a Grant to one of us (R. E. C.).

REFERENCES

1. KUHN, KUENZLE, and KATCHALSKY, *Bull. Soc. Chim. Belgique* **57**, 421 (1948); HERMANS and OVERBEEK, *ibid.* 154; *Rec. Trav. Chim. Pays Bas* **67**, 761 (1948); KATCHALSKY, KUENZLE and KUHN, *J. Polymer Sci.* **5**, 283 (1950); KUENZLE, *Rec. Trav. Chim. Pays Bas* **68**, 699 (1949); ARNOLD and OVERBEEK, *ibid* **69**, 192 (1950); MARKOWITZ and KIMBALL, *Colloid Sci.* **5**, 115 (1950); KATCHALSKY and EISENBERG, *J. Polymer Sci.* **5**, 285 (1950).
2. The increase of the viscosity of polyacids with increasing pH has been observed by STAUDINGER, *Die Hochmolekularen Organischen Verbindungen*, Berlin, Springer, 1932, p. 363; STAUDINGER and TROMMSDORF, *Ann*, **502**, 201 (1933); KERN, *Z. Phys. Chem.* A **181**, 283 (1938), but the correct interpretation has not been given by these authors.
3. FUOSS and STRAUSS, *J. Polymer Sci.* **3**, 602 (1948); *Ann. N.Y. Acad. Sci.* **51**, 836 (1948); FUOSS, *J. Polymer Sci.* **3**, 603 (1948); FUOSS and CATHERS, *ibid.* **4**, 112 (1949).
4. KATCHALSKY, *J. Polymer Sci.* **7**, 397 (1951); HARKNESS and WASSERMANN, *J. Chem. Soc.* 1344 (1954).
5. KUHN, *Experientia* **5**, 318 (1949); KATCHALSKY, *ibid.* 319; BREITENBACH and KARLINGER, *Monatsh.* **80**, 311 (1949); KUHN, HARGITAY, KATCHALSKY, and EISENBERG, *Nature* **165**, 515 (1950) and other papers cited in ref 2. Paper by KATCHALSKY *et al.* of this volume, cf. also FLORY, *Principles of Polymer Chemistry*, Cornell University Press, 1953, pp. 584–593, and reference 9–11; Paper by KUHN *et al.* of this volume.
6. *Biochem. Z.* **214**, 272 (1929).
7. HARKNESS and WASSERMANN, *J. Chem. Soc.* 497 (1952).

8. MONGAR and WASSERMANN, *Nature* **159**, 746 (1947); *Disc. Faraday Soc.* **7**, 118 (1949); *J. Chem. Soc.* 492, 500 (1952); MACARTHUR, MONGAR, and WASSERMANN, *Nature* **164**, 110 (1949).

9. See, for instance, GUSTAVSON, *The Chemistry and Reactivity of Collagens*, Academic Press, New York, p. 211, 1956.

10. RUDALL, *Symposium on Fibrous Proteins*, Society of Dyers and Colourists, 1946, p. 15.

11. OTH and FLORY, *J. Am. Chem. Soc.* **80**, 1297 (1958).

12. MANDELKERN, RUDALL, DIORIO and POSNER, *J. Am. Chem. Soc.* **81**, 4148 (1959).

13. HIRST, JONES, and JONES, *J. Chem. Soc.* 1880 (1939); ASTBURY, *Nature* **155**, 667 (1945). Another repeating unit is l-guluronic acid; see FISCHER and DOERFEL, *Z. physiol. Chem.* **302**, 186 (1955).

14. DEUEL and SOLMS, *Kolloid Z.* **124**, 65 (1951); WALL and DRENAN, *J. Polymer Sci.* **7**, 83 (1951).

15. COOPER, Ph.D. Thesis, London, 1958.

16. FOX, FOX, and FLORY, *J. Am. Chem. Soc.* **73**, 1901 (1953).

17. See, for instance, OGSTON and STANIER, *Biochem. J.* **53**, 4 (1953).

18. HUGGINS, *J. Amer. Chem. Soc.* **64**, 2716 (1942).

19. See, for instance, ROSE, Ph.D. Thesis, London, 1937.

20. *Can. J. Research* **28B**, 105 (1950).

21. OVERBECK and VAN GEELEN; paper read on September 16th 1958 (see *Trans. Faraday Soc.* **55**, 363) (1959).

22. See, for instance, STOCKMAYER and FIXMAN, *Ann. N.Y. Acad. Sci.* **57**, 341 (1953).

23. ZIMM and STOCKMAYER, *J. Chem. Phys.* **17**, 1301 (1949); THURMOND and ZIMM, *J. Polymer Sci.* **8**, 494 (1952); ZIMM and KILB, *J. Polymer Sci.*, **37**, 19, (1959); KILB, *ibid*, **38**, 403 (1959).

24. FLORY, *J. Am. Chem. Soc.* **63**, 3083, 3091, 3096 (1941); STOCKMAYER, *J. Chem. Physics* **11**, 45 (1943); **12**, 125 (1944).

6

THE HIGH-ENERGY PHOSPHATE BOND CONCEPT

by C. A. VERNON

*William Ramsay and Ralph Forster Laboratories,
University College, London*

THE CONCEPT of the "high-energy phosphate bond", which was introduced by Lipmann in 1941,[1] is now used so frequently that some understanding of it is important to all who have occasion to read the biochemical literature. The concept has its origin in the discovery that adenosine triphosphate (ATP) is important in metabolic processes. It is now well known that carbohydrate breakdown involves the production of ATP which is utilized in many synthetic reactions. For example, the anaerobic degradation of glucose to lactic acid as it occurs in muscle can be represented by the stoicheiometric equation[2]

$$C_6H_{12}O_6 + 2ADP + 2H_3PO_4 = 2CH_3CH(OH)COOH \\ + 2ATP + 2H_2O \quad (1)$$

so that 2 moles of ATP are produced for the degradation of 1 mole of glucose. On the other hand, the synthesis of urea can be represented by,[3]

$$2NH_3 + CO_2 + 2ATP + H_2O = CO(NH_2)_2 + 2ADP \\ + 2H_3PO_4 \quad (2)$$

and 2 moles of ATP are used up for each mole of urea produced. In an important sense ATP is the "linking agent" between anabolic and catabolic processes—it is the means whereby the breakdown of foodstuffs is "geared" to many of the vital synthetic activities which take place in living tissue.

A common conceptual device is to separate anabolic and catabolic processes and, remembering that the former proceed with a decrease in standard free energy whereas the latter, for the most part, involve an increase in standard free energy, to suppose that one set of processes "drives" the other. It is then an obvious move to say that, since ATP is clearly an important linking substance, the energy derived from the breakdown of carbohydrates is somehow stored in the ATP and then utilized to drive synthetic reactions as required. Such a view is not unacceptable at an elementary level. It is consistent with the commonly-drawn analogy between living organisms and heat engines, as expressed, for example, in the description of foodstuffs as "fuels" and of the oxidation of carbohydrates as the "burning of fuels". In the high-energy phosphate bond theory this elementary viewpoint is used as a conceptual basis for the manipulation of thermodynamic data. The resulting hybrid is an unfortunate one and, as we shall see, leads to a highly misleading picture of the chemical organization present in living tissue.

The theory starts from the observation that the hydrolysis of ATP under conditions which are directly relevant to biochemistry proceeds with a large decrease in standard free energy (ΔG^0). The exact value of ΔG^0 has been the subject of considerable controversy but we need not be concerned with this. The important points are that ΔG^0 is negative, fairly large and certainly larger than the corresponding values for most simple phosphate esters. The subject has been recently reviewed by Burton[4] who concludes that, at pH 7·4 and with 1 M concentrations of the phosphorus containing components as standard state, the reaction

$$ATP^{4-} + H_2O \longrightarrow ADP^{3-} + HPO_4^{2-} + H^+ \tag{3}$$

has $\Delta G^0 = -8·4$ kcal/mole. The corresponding values for simple phosphate esters are usually supposed to be in the range -2 to -4 kcal/mole. Now consider the stoicheiometric equation representing the synthesis of urea in living tissue (equation 2). For thermodynamic purposes, since standard free energies are additive, this equation may be regarded as the sum of two other stoicheiometric equations representing, respectively, the direct synthesis of urea from ammonia and carbon dioxide (both in aqueous solution) and the hydrolysis of two moles of ATP.*

* For convenience the ionization of the acidic groups has been ignored in writing equation (5), and this practice will be adopted throughout. The value of $\Delta G^0 = -8·4$ kcal/mole, however, applies to equation (3) *as written*.

$$2NH_3 + CO_2 = CO(NH_2)_2 + H_2O \qquad (4)$$

$$2ATP + 2H_2O = 2ADP + 2H_3PO_4 \qquad (5)$$

Addition of (4) and (5) gives (2) and hence

$$\Delta G_2^0 = \Delta G_4^0 + \Delta G_5^0$$

where the numerical subscripts denote the appropriate reactions. Now ΔG_4^0 is positive; i.e., the equilibrium position for reaction (4) favours, under the relevant conditions, the hydrolysis rather than the synthesis of urea. The value of ΔG_5^0 is, however, large and negative; i.e., $-2 \times 8 \cdot 4$ kcal/mole. Given that $|\Delta G_5^0| > |G_4^0|$ it follows, therefore, that ΔG_2^0 is negative; i.e., the equilibrium position of reaction (2) favours the right-hand side. This means that whereas the synthesis of urea cannot occur to any appreciable extent by a process which is represented simply by equation (4), it can occur by a process represented by equation (2). In the language of the "high-energy phosphate bond theory" this is expressed by saying that the hydrolysis of ATP, (5), *"drives"* the synthesis of urea, (4); or in free energy terms, that the free energy made available by the hydrolysis of ATP is utilized for the synthesis of urea, the whole process being represented by equation (2). This idea can be generalized. If

$$A + B \longrightarrow S \qquad (\Delta G_s^0) \qquad (6)*$$

represents a synthetic process for which ΔG_s^0 is positive and if the biosynthesis of S conforms to the equation,

$$A + B + xATP + xH_2O \longrightarrow S + xADP$$
$$+ xH_3PO_4 \qquad (\Delta G_B^0) \qquad (7)$$

then the synthesis of S is achieved in reasonable yield if

$$|\Delta G_s^0| < |x \cdot 8 \cdot 4|.$$

In such a case the free energy of hydrolysis of ATP is said to be utilized in the synthesis of S.†

---

* Such equations are frequently, as in the case of urea, representative of the reverse of a hydrolytic process.

† The idea may be further generalized since the *"driving"* equation need not be the hydrolysis of ATP but any other reaction for which the standard free energy charge is large and negative.

The next step in this approach is to introduce the idea of *efficiency*. If, since for synthesis of S it is necessary only that ΔG_B^0 be negative, for example in the above scheme $x = 1$ and $\Delta G_s^0 = +2,000$ kcal/mole, then *ca.* 6,000 kcal/mole of free energy have been "wasted". Or, put in another way, a process for which $x = 1$ is less efficient than one in which, say $x = \frac{1}{3}$. This idea can be applied, in an exactly analogous way, to those processes which produce ATP. The basic concept is that the free energy of hydrolysis of ATP is the fundamental energy "currency" of living tissue. The free energy of the degradation of glucose is converted into it and it is then used, as required, for synthetic purposes. Given this standpoint the efficiency of the conversion processes is an intelligible concept.

It is, of course, easy enough to understand the application of these views to the problem of muscular contraction. It appears that ATP breakdown is one of the steps involved in this process and is presumably brought about by the adenosine triphosphatase of the myofibril. It may be said, therefore, in the language of the high-energy phosphate bond theory, that the free energy of hydrolysis of ATP is converted, in the muscle, directly into mechanical energy. In this way the theory provides a common basis for diverse "energy-consuming" processes. The common factor is the free energy stored in ATP. This represents the available energy store of a living organism and given suitable pathways, it may be converted into mechanical energy or used to "drive" synthetic processes.

There has been a tendency to interpret the language of the "high energy phosphate bond theory" in rather a literal way. For example, it is often implied that if energy is stored in ATP it must be stored somewhere. Since, on hydrolysis, the energy is liberated it must have been stored in the phosphorus–oxygen bond which undergoes fission. To indicate this a special symbol is sometimes used. A "high-energy bond" is denoted as, for example, $P \sim O$, in contrast to an ordinary bond, P—O, which does not contain a great store of energy. This move has been heavily criticized by several authors[5, 6] and need not unduly concern us. The phrase "high-energy phosphate bond" need only mean that the phosphate ester under discussion has a standard free energy of hydrolysis which is large and negative.

The theory may be summarized as follows, (a) ATP is produced by catabolic processes. The free energy of such processes is, thereby, converted into the free energy of hydrolysis of ATP. The efficiency of the conversion is obtained by separation of the whole process into two parts, one of which represents the degradative steps and the other the synthesis of ATP by the reverse of its hydrolysis. Comparison of the standard free energy changes of the two parts then gives the efficiency. (b) The free energy of hydrolysis of ATP is used to "drive" "energy-consuming processes". In the case of synthetic processes the efficiency is obtained, as above, by comparing the standard free energy changes of the two components into which the whole process may be separated, i.e. the "direct" synthesis and the hydrolysis of ATP.

Certain general criticisms of the theory may be made immediately. Firstly, the data used are *standard* free energy changes and do not, therefore, measure the *actual* free energy changes associated with particular reactions as they occur under biological conditions. In a sense, ΔG^0 values refer to hypothetical processes and not to ones which actually occur. Secondly, the addition of standard free energy changes for a series of chemical reactions is simply equivalent to the process of calculating the equilibrium constants for some reactions from the known values of others. In this context, ΔG^0 is a mathematical parameter which, because of its additive properties is more conveniently handled than the equilibrium constant, K. The language of the "high-energy phosphate bond theory", however, gives to ΔG^0 the status of a physically real entity. It is imagined as a kind of energy which may be transferred from molecule to molecule, with greater or smaller amount of loss, down a reaction sequence. For example, Baldwin[7] in describing the terminal phosphate radical of ATP says that it "can be transferred, *together with a part or all of the . . . free energy with which it is associated,* to other molecules". This view of the status of standard free energy is wholly misleading.

The limitations of the theory are, however, more strikingly seen by considering, in some detail, some of the synthetic reactions which are known to be mediated by ATP. It is not possible to reduce all of these to a common pattern but it is clear, from, for example, the excellent account given by Dixon,[8] that there are a considerable number conforming to the general stiocheiometric equation,

$$X—OH + Y—H + ATP = X—Y + ADP + H_3PO_4 \qquad (8)$$

in which the species X—Y is synthesized at the expense of ATP. Two steps are involved. Firstly, the species X—OH is phosphorylated by ATP.

$$X—OH + ATP = X—OPO_3H_2 + ADP \qquad (9)$$

Secondly, the phosphate ester of X—OH, so produced, condenses with YH giving the species X—Y with elimination of the phosphate radical.

$$X—OPO_3H_2 + YH = X—Y + H_3PO_4 \qquad (10)$$

The first reaction is catalysed by a phosphokinase, the second by a phosphorylase. The synthesis of sucrose in bacteria (X—OH is glucose, YH is fructose) may proceed in this way and the synthesis of starch and glycogen, although involving more steps, is of the same general kind. An important variant involves the transfer of a pyrophosphate rather than a phosphate radical in the first step and a number of nucleosides are apparently synthesized in this way.[9] The general stoicheiometric equation for such processes is

$$X—OH + Y—H + ATP = X—Y + AMP + H_4P_2O_7 \quad (11)$$

For simplicity only processes conforming to equation (8) will be explicitly considered. No loss of generality is incurred by this, however, since processes which involve steps additional to (9) and (10), (such as the synthesis of glycogen), or which conform to equation (11) can be discussed in an exactly analogous way.

Now equation (8) is obtained by adding equations (9) and (10) thence the total standard free energy change (ΔG_8) can be calculated from the standard free energy changes of the two component reactions.

$$\Delta G_8^0 = \Delta G_9^0 + \Delta G_{10}^0.$$

Equation (8) can also be obtained by adding the two equations (12) and (13).

$$X—OH + Y—H = X—Y + H_2O \qquad (12)$$

$$ATP + H_2O = ADP + H_3PO_4 \qquad (13)$$

where these represent respectively the "direct" condensation of X—OH and Y—H and the hydrolysis of ATP. As before, the total standard free energy change can be calculated from the standard free energy changes of the two component reactions and, therefore,

$$\Delta G_8^0 = \Delta G_{12}^0 + \Delta G_{13}^0.$$

In the high-energy phosphate bond theory it is the second of these two addition processes which is considered important. There are two reasons for this. Firstly, the value of ΔG_{12}^0 is, in many cases, known thence ΔG_8^0 is easily found. Secondly, and possibly more important, a comparison of equations (12) and (8) represents a comparison of the "direct" and "biological" synthesis of X—Y. It is often the case that ΔG_{12}^0 is positive (0 to $+ 6,000$ kcal/mole) and hence the "direct" synthesis of X—Y is a process which does not result in a high yield in product. However, since ΔG_{13}^0 has a high negative value, ΔG_8^0 will, in general, be negative, hence the synthesis of X—Y, as mediated by ATP, results in a high yield of product and is, therefore, a biologically useful process. Why is it that one process is favourable for the synthesis of X—Y and the other is not? In the terminology of the high-energy phosphate bond theory the reason is that ΔG_{13}^0 (the standard free energy of hydrolysis of ATP) is large and negative and it is this free energy which "drives" the synthesis.

Now there is an important difference between expressing equation (8), on the one hand as the sum of equations (9) and (10) and on the other, as the sum of equations (12) and (13). In a solution initially containing the species X—OH, YH, ATP and enzymes catalysing the processes represented by (9) and (10), the overall reaction will conform to the stoicheiometry of equation (8), that is, one g-mole of X—Y will be produced for every g-mole of ATP which disappears. In other words, equation (8) describes the *actual* result of allowing (9) and (10) to occur together. Furthermore, given, that (9) and (10) are the only processes taking place then the overall reaction is necessarily represented by equation (8)—no other stoicheiometry is possible. If, however, again starting with a solution containing X—OH, Y—H and ATP, and this time with enzymes catalysing processes (12) and (13), the overall reaction will *not* conform to equation (8). Instead the two equilibria represented by (12) and (13) will be established independently and the proportion of X—Y formed will be governed solely by the equilibrium constant of equation (12). Reactions (12) and (13) are not linked in any way and if allowed to occur in the same solution will proceed independently. Reactions (9) and (10), on the other hand, are linked together since the product of one reaction is the substrate for the other. It follows from this that one of the conditions for the occurrence of reaction (8) is that reactions (12) and (13) must *not* take place. The presence in the system of an active enzyme hydrolysing ATP will prevent the synthesis of X—Y. As far as metabolic processes are concerned, therefore, ATP hydrolysis must be regarded as an uncoupling reaction which competes with, and if sufficiently catalysed will completely prevent, the various synthetic reactions which involve ATP.

The addition of equations (12) and (13) is, therefore, only a computational device by which the two chemical equations are manipulated as if they were algebraic equations. Since, as we have seen, the reactions (12) and (13) must not occur if the synthesis of X—Y is to proceed, we shall call these reactions *pseudomeric* reactions (i.e. false components). It is obvious that we could divide equation (8) into other pseudomers: the main reason for the usual choice of (12) and (13) is simply that the value for the standard free energy change of (13) happens to be known.

This point can also be illustrated by considering equation (9). This equation, which represents a process in which an alcohol, X—OH, is phosphorylated by ATP, can be obtained by addition of the two equations,

$$\text{ATP} + \text{H}_2\text{O} = \text{ADP} + \text{H}_3\text{PO}_4 \tag{13}$$

$$\text{X—OH} + \text{H}_3\text{PO}_4 = \text{X—OPO}_3\text{H}_2 + \text{H}_2\text{O} \tag{14}$$

where (14) represents the hydrolysis of the phosphate, $\text{X—OPO}_3\text{H}_2$, written in reverse and (13), as before, represents the hydrolysis of ATP. If, as is often the case, the standard free energy change for the hydrolysis of $\text{X—OPO}_3\text{H}_2$ is known, then the standard free energy change for equation (9) is easily found. However, processes (13) and (14) are pseudomeric: if they actually take place they will compete with process (9) and if sufficiently catalysed will prevent it entirely. Furthermore, it is easy to construct other pseudomeric reactions. For example, the ethanolysis of $\text{X—OPO}_3\text{H}_2$ and of ATP can be written as two equations whose sum gives equation (9). There is, therefore, no virtue in any view which gives special importance in relation to reaction (9) to the free energy of hydrolysis of ATP.

These considerations apply generally to any biochemical process involving ATP or any other "high-energy" phosphate ester. If the overall stoicheiometric equation is split up in such a way that one of the component equations represents the hydrolysis of ATP then the whole set is pseudomeric and each of the pseudomeric processes will be forbidden, i.e. must not occur if the total process is to take place. The set of pseudomeric equations which includes ATP hydrolysis will not be the only possible set and, therefore, any calculations of the efficiency of utilization of the free energy of ATP will depend upon the set chosen. The peculiarity of the "high-energy phosphate bond" theory is that it confuses a computational device with a physical process. Standard free energies of hydrolysis are useful in that they can be used in the calculation of equilibrium constants, but it is not a useful concept to select one of these and elevate it to the status of the "driving-force" behind metabolic processes.

Now the addition of pseudomeric reactions is a thermodynamically valid procedure. Consequently, there must be a way of carrying out the total process such that these reactions become the true components. For example, process (8) actually occurs, in living tissue, by the reactions (9) and (10); reactions (12) and (13) are, therefore, pseudomeric. But since the addition of (12) and (13) is algebraically equivalent to (8) there must be a way of carrying out process (8) by actually using the two reactions represented by (9) and (10). It is of interest to examine how this could be done. If chemical cells were constructed such that their operation corresponded to equations (13) and (12), i.e., to the hydrolysis of ATP and of X—Y respectively, and if the potential of one cell were used to reverse the spontaneous chemical change in the other then the overall process would be as represented by equation (8) and, under these conditions, reactions (12) and (13) would be the true components and not pseudomers. Furthermore, the potential of the cell in which ATP hydrolysis occurs could be used to reverse the spontaneous chemical change in a number of the other cells connected in series and, in these circumstances, the g-mole yield of X—Y in terms of ATP could be made larger than unity. It would then be sensible to discuss the efficiency of utilization of the free energy of hydrolysis of ATP.

Such systems might be said to be *energy-linked*. Metabolic processes, however, are not like this. Reaction (8), for example, occurs in living tissue because one of the products of reaction (9) is one of the substrates for reaction (10). Such systems might be said to be *chemically-linked*. The "high-energy phosphate bond" theory, with its emphasis on ATP hydrolysis, discusses metabolic processes as if they were divisible into energy-linked reactions. This is not the case. The use of the language of the theory, apart from generating a belief in fictitious kinds of chemical bonds, serves to direct attention away from the actual steps of metabolic processes. It is by a study of these steps and particularly of their organization and control that metabolic processes are to be understood. The "high-energy phosphate bond" theory would be an appropriate intellectual framework if metabolic reactions were energy-linked. But they are not. They are linked in such a way that the utilization and production of ATP, in so far as these concepts are important, should be specified in material units, i.e. as g-moles of ATP per g-mole of some other substance or substances. The continued use of the phrase "high-energy phosphate bond" will add nothing to the understanding of biochemical processes and will serve simply as a centre of confusion.

REFERENCES

1. LIPMANN, *Advances in Enzymology*, **1**, 99 (1941).
2. DIXON and WEBB, *The Enzymes*, Longmans, p. 588, 1958.
3. Ref. 2, p. 608.
4. BURTON, *Nature* **181**, 1594 (1958).
5. GILLESPIE, MAW, and VERNON, *Nature* **171**, 1147 (1953).
6. HILL and MORALES, *J. Am. Chem. Soc.* **73**, 1656 (1951).
7. BALDWIN, *Organic Aspects of Biochemistry*, Cambridge University Press, p. 70, 1952.
8. DIXON, *Multienzyme Systems*, Cambridge University Press, 1951.
9. Ref. 2, pp. 220, 221.